Bumper
Quiz
Book

Bumper
Quiz
Book

by

Cockerill and Jace

List of Subjects

Abbreviations

1. Which sporting organisation is known by the initials AAA?
2. BLAISE may be helpful to the researcher or student. What is it?
3. What do the initials ABTA mean?
4. The ACTT is the union of which group of employees?
5. The suffix AD after a date signals Anno Domini – what does Anno Domini mean?
6. AIDS is a killer disease which breaks down the body's natural defences against illness. What do the letters of the abbreviation mean?
7. ANZAC is associated with the Gallipoli landings in World War I. What do the initials ANZAC stand for?
8. What do the initials APT represent in connection with British Rail?
9. The ATS was formed in 1938. What was this women's service?
10. What is the meaning of the military acronym AWACS?
11. Which awards are known by the abbreviation BAFTA?
12. What is BASIC in computer language?
13. Whom might you be visiting if they were a member of the BDA?
14. What do the initials BST represent?
15. If you belonged to the organisation CARD, what cause would you support?
16. What, in computer terminology, do the initials COBOL mean?

17. With what is the CPRE concerned?
18. Washington is the capital of the United States of America. What do the letters DC after Washington mean?
19. What do the initials DPP mean?
20. Amongst his many honours, Douglas Bader held the DSO and the DFC. What do these initials represent?
21. What do the initials DSS mean?
22. What is the meaning of the abbreviation DVLC?
23. Which department of a hospital is known by the initials ENT?
24. What is the meaning of the abbreviation EPNS?
25. The name Ernie is used to describe the machine which selects Premium Bond winners. What do the letters ERNIE stand for?
26. What is ESP?
27. What would a person be a fellow of if they had the initials FBAA after their name?
28. In England and Wales, what do the initials FCA represent in connection with the accountancy profession?
29. If someone had the initials FRIBA after his name, to what profession would he belong?
30. If a person had the initials FRCVS after his name, to what profession would he belong?
31. American servicemen during the Second World War were known as GIs. What did these initials stand for?
32. What do the initials HMSO mean?
33. What do the initials IQ mean?
34. The IOC is concerned with organising a sporting event held every four years. What do these initials mean?
35. In the history of British Regiments for what did KOSB stand?
36. In the world of politics, for what do the initials MEP stand?
37. What is the meaning of the acronym MIDAS?
38. What is the meaning of the abbreviation NAAFI?
39. NASA is the American government's agency for

civilian space flight. What do the initials represent?

40. What do the initials NATO mean?
41. Which international organisation is known by the acronym OPEC?
42. What do the initials PVC mean?
43. What does the acronym QUANGO stand for?
44. What do the initials RADA represent?
45. What do the initials RSPCA mean?
46. What do the initials RSVP mean?
47. What does the following abbreviation represent: ISBN?
48. SPCK has bookshops around Britain. What do its initials represent?
49. Which organisation was named SEATO?
50. What is TIROS?
51. What do the initials TNT mean?
52. In France what do the initials TGV mean?
53. What do the initials UFO mean?
54. What do the initials UNESCO represent?
55. With what is the United Nations organisation UNICEF concerned?
56. What does the following abbreviation represent: VIP?
57. What do the initials VHF mean in connection with radio?
58. A helicopter is a VTOL vehicle. What do these initials represent?
59. Which organisation is known by the initials YHA?
60. What do the initials YMCA mean?

Animal World : Names

1. Name the national bird of New Zealand.
2. What type of animal is known by the name Dobbin?
3. What is the name of the smallest bird in the world?

4. What word collectively describes the following different animals: beaver, porcupine, hare, lemming, squirrel, water-vole and guinea-pig?

5. The slow-worm is incorrectly named in that it is not a worm. What is it?

6. What is the name of the only venomous snake in Britain?

7. What is the name of the breed of short-haired German terrier with blunt nose and erect ears, often used as a guard dog?

8. What animal, present in large numbers in Australia, is known to native Australians as a 'jumbuck'?

9. A group of deer is known as a herd. What is the group name given to insects?

10. What is the correct name for the bird that sailors sometimes call Mother Carey's Chicken?

11. It is a large humped animal with long silky hair, found wild and domesticated in Tibet and other high regions of Central Asia – name it.

12. A female fox is known as a vixen; what is a male fox called?

13. What names are given to the male and the female swan?

14. Pulex Irritans is a parasitic insect – by what name is it more commonly known?

15. What name is given to the larvae of flies?

16. What is the name of the small German dog with long body, drooping ears and short legs?

17. What is the name of the only Irish pony?

18. By what name are the semi-domesticated dogs kept by the Eskimos known?

19. The crane-fly has a nickname which describes its appearance very accurately – what is its nickname?

20. What is a female donkey called?

21. Name the only armoured mammal, which is related to the sloths and ant-eaters.

22. What name is popularly given to a baby kangaroo?

23. Which animal has the types Barn, Snowy, Eagle,

Long-eared?
24. Which animal is the offspring of a male ass and a mare?
25. What is a male honey-bee known as?
26. What is the breed of dog which has a wiry black and tan coat and is the largest in the terrier group?
27. What is the name of the only monkey which is a native of Europe?
28. By what name do we know the domesticated albino variety of polecat?
29. What creature takes the following forms during its life: 'parr', 'smolt' and 'grilse'?
30. Which massive horse was once called the 'Great Horse of England'?
31. What name is given to a young hawk taken from its nest for training, or not yet completely trained?
32. What type of animal is an eland?
33. What is a young hare called?
34. Name the largest living invertebrate.
35. Antlers are normally grown only by the male of the deer family but two species of deer are the exception, in that the female also grows antlers. Name one of these deer species.
36. What is the name of the South American animal related to the Llama whose long fine wool is woven into soft dress fabric?
37. Two of the most important breeds of dairy cattle come from the Channel Islands. What are the names of these breeds?
38. Spider, hermit and masked are types of which creature?
39. Which animal, now almost extinct, was considered the King of the Indian Jungle?
40. What name is given to the lively squirrel with dark stripes running down its back which spends most of its time on the ground?
41. Which animal is known as 'the ship of the desert'?
42. Name the two types of camel.

Animal World : Physical Matters

1. How many stomachs has a cow?
2. A bee has an odd number of eyes – how many?
3. What are the three jointed parts of an insect's body called?
4. How many legs has a lobster?
5. What is the name given to the short tail of a rabbit?
6. What colour spots has the common ladybird?
7. If an animal was described as ungulate what would be its distinguishing feature?
8. What is the gestation period of a cow?
9. A horse's height is measured from the ground to which part of its body?
10. Which breed of sheep, originally from Spain, is noted for its fine silky wool?
11. What animal's skin gives us Morocco Leather?
12. How many tentacles has the cuttle fish?
13. How many arms does a starfish usually have?
14. What is the distinctive physical feature of the Proboscis Monkey?
15. From what kind of animal is cat-gut obtained?
16. How do hummingbirds make their characteristic sound?
17. What is the gestation period of an elephant?
18. What do the greyhound, deerhound and wolfhound all have in common?
19. What is the correct name for a bird's feathers?

Animal World : The Most

1. Which are the most dangerous insects in the world? (If we exclude wars and accidents they have probably been responsible directly or indirectly for 50% of all human deaths since the Stone Age.)
2. What is the largest known mammal which reaches a length of 100 ft?
3. Which is the most poisonous, as opposed to venomous, fish in the world?
4. The cheetah is the fastest thing on four legs. What is reputed to be the fastest thing on two legs?
5. Which is the most widely distributed of all mammals? It is found on every continent, including Antarctica.
6. Which is the smallest reptile found in Britain?
7. What is generally regarded as the world's tallest breed of dog?
8. Which bird has the longest wing span of any living bird?
9. Which animal has the heaviest brain in the animal world and the most complex?
10. What is generally regarded as being the longest lived of all animals?
11. What is the fastest wild mammal found in Britain?
12. What is the largest reptile (excluding snakes) found in Britain?

Animal World : What Is It?

1. What type of creature is a sidewinder?
2. What type of animal was a mammoth?
3. Which animal has breeds called Rex, Netherlands Dwarf, Satin and Dutch?
4. What kind of creatures live in a formicary?
5. What is a papillon?
6. What is a rhea?
7. It's a type of brilliantly coloured insect with large net veined wings which eats other insects caught during flight. In Scotland it is known as the Devil's Darning Needle. What insect is it?
8. What are manatees and dugongs?
9. What type of dog is a Cardigan?
10. What are polled cattle?
11. What is a terrapin?
12. What kind of birds are Cushat, Rock and Stock?
13. What is a chuckwalla?
14. Water, Common and Pygmy are kinds of which mammal found in England?
15. What is a jackal?
16. What kind of animal is a pangolin?
17. What type of animal is a bariroussa?
18. What is a taipan?
19. A quadruped is a four-footed animal. What is a palmiped?
20. What type of animal is a Falabella?
21. What kind of creature was Riki Tiki Tavi?
22. What is a natterjack?
23. What is a marmoset?

24. In Scotland, which animals are sometimes referred to as bubbly-jocks?
25. It is a mammal, native to South Africa, with a Dutch name meaning earth-pig. One of its most distinctive features is an extensile tongue. What animal is it?
26. Which animal, at one time native to the British Isles, became extinct in Scotland in 1743 and in Ireland in 1766?
27. What kind of creature was Captain Flint?
28. What is an impala?
29. What is a flying fox?
30. To which family of birds does the greenshank belong?
31. What type of animal is a markhor?
32. Which Scottish game bird was extinct in Britain for 200 years but was successfully re-introduced from Sweden?
33. What are animals called that are able to live on land or in water?
34. The order *Chiroptera* have species with the following distinctive names – Natterer's, Bechstein's, Noctule and Barbastrelle. By what name are they more commonly, collectively, called?
35. The Redwing, Fieldfare and Ring Ouzel all belong to which large family of birds?

Animal World :
Where In The World?

1. In which country does the wild dog known as the dingo live?
2. The grey squirrel is not an indigenous British mammal but was introduced from abroad in 1889. From which part of the world was it introduced?

3. In which European city would you find the famous white horses of the Spanish Riding School?
4. Friesian cattle are called after the province of Friesland – in which country is Friesland?
5. Where in the world would you find budgerigars in their natural habitat?
6. Where in the world would you find a vicuna and an alpaca?
7. Where is the largest nature reserve in Great Britain?
8. With what country is the breed of dogs known as corgis associated?
9. The peacock is the national bird of which country?
10. A chihuahua dog derives its name from a town. In which country is the town?
11. Where in the world would you find a bandicoot?
12. From which country did the turkey originate?

Art

1. Who painted *The Birth Of Venus* and *Mars And Venus*?
2. Which artist was the inventor of the pointilliste technique, where he built up large-scale paintings from tiny dots?
3. *The Scourging of Christ* and *The Disrobing of Christ* are among the masterpieces of which artist?
4. Which artist do you associate with the painting *Flatford Mill*?
5. The *Rouen Cathedral* series was among the works of which leading French Impressionist painter?
6. Which sculptor's works include *Genesis* (1931), *Adam* (1939) and *Lucifer* (1945)?

7. *Snow Storm – Steam-Boat Off A Harbour's Mouth* was a seascape by which English artist?
8. What style of painting was exhibited in Paris by Monet, Renoir and Degas in 1874?
9. Which famous French painter's works include *The Bathers*, *La Loge* and *Les Parapluies*?
10. Which eighteenth century artist's works include *Age Of Innocence*, *Captain Robert Orme* and *Lady Cockburn*?
11. Which painter do you associate with the famous paintings *Crucifixion* and *The Persistence of Memory*?
12. Canaletto, born in 1697, is most famous for his superb landscapes of two cities – name one of them.
13. Whom do you associate with the famous painting called *Sunflowers*?
14. Who painted *The Laughing Cavalier*?
15. What was the name of the British artist who painted the 80th birthday portrait of Sir Winston Churchill for Parliament?
16. Which American artist do you associate with the work entitled, *Arrangement in Grey and Black – The Artist's Mother*?
17. Which Italian painter do you associate with the work *Venice: A Regatta On The Grand Canal*?
18. What famous painting is otherwise known as *La Gioconda*?
19. Which artist's famous work *Guernica* expresses his horror at the outrages of the Spanish Civil War?
20. Which artist from the Netherlands painted *The Marriage of Giovannia Arnolfini*?
21. Which twentieth century artist in his studio, The Factory, mass-produced art screen prints of soup cans and film stars?
22. Which Flemish painter do you associate with *Adoration of the Kings* and *Wedding Dance*?
23. Sir Edwin Landseer was a famous English artist. In what particular subject did he specialise?
24. Which French artist painted *The Harvest*?

25. With what type of paintings do you associate the names of Nicholas Hilliard, Richard Cosway and George Engleheart?

26. Which English sculptor's works included *Reclining Figure* (1951)?

27. Who aroused a storm of controversy with his painting *Christ in the House of His Parents*?

28. Which Belgian artist do you associate with *Charles I Of England*?

29. Who is the twentieth century Australian painter, once a professional cyclist, who made his name with a series of paintings about the criminal Ned Kelly?

30. Which Italian painter do you associate with *Coronation Of The Virgin*, *Peita* and *Agony In The Garden*?

31. Who was the French painter (1864–1901) who was the first to make the poster a serious work of art?

32. A Dutch painter and etcher, he was born in Lieden, the son of a miller, and some of his most famous paintings include *The Night Watch*, *The Mill*, and *Christ Healing*. Who was he?

33. What is the correct title for the painting known as the *Rokeby Venus* by the Spanish painter Velázquez?

34. Paul Gauguin – the post-impressionist French artist – devoted much of his life to painting scenes of a South Sea Island. Which island did he often paint?

35. Which artist, sculptor and architect designed the Dome of St Peter's in Rome?

36. *Vision of a Knight* was the work of which Florentine painter?

37. Who was the French painter and sculptor whose work included *The Pink Nude*?

38. Which French artist do you associate with the painting *Luncheon Of The Boating Party*?

39. Who painted *Virgin on the Rocks* between 1483–1506?

40. Which Italian painter do you associate with *The Tribute Money* and *Bacchus And Ariadne*?

41. *An Interior with a Woman Drinking with Two Men, and a Maidservant* was the title of a work by which

Dutch painter?

42. Who painted the portrait of Squire Hallet and his wife entitled *The Morning Walk*?

43. The English artist Stubbs was most famous for portraying what specific subjects?

44. Who was the artist who painted the controversial portrait of Mrs Thatcher entitled *Welcome to Kuala Lumpur* which shows Mrs Thatcher as haughty, squinty eyed and with buck teeth?

45. What name is given to the famous statue which is located at the entrance to Copenhagen Harbour?

46. Which French artist is best known for his studies of peasants such as *The Reapers* (1854), *The Gleaners* (1857) and *The Angelus* (1859)?

47. Which English painter modelled the group of lions at the base of Nelson's Column in Trafalgar Square, London?

48. Which English painter illustrated the dead rising from their tombs in Cookham churchyard in his work *The Resurrection*?

49. Which sculptor created the famous work entitled *The Thinker*?

50. Which artist of the Venetian school painted the magnificent picture *The Feast of the Gods* when he was over eighty years old?

51. Who was the French artist (1834–1917) known for his paintings of the ballet and ballet dancers?

52. Sir Alfred Gilbert was an English sculptor whose best-known work stands in the middle of Piccadilly Circus. What is the statue known as?

53. Where in London would you find Eric Gill's sculpture of *Prospero and Ariel*?

54. What name is given to the style of art invented by Picasso and Braque in which the subject is reduced to basic geometric solids?

The Arts

1. What is the name given to the craft or art which involves the inlay of ornamental woods, metals, shells, ivory, etc. cut thin, and glued onto wood and furniture?
2. What was the name of the leading family in Florence during the Renaissance who were responsible for the building of huge palaces and churches and promoting painting and sculpture?
3. With which branch of the arts was the Russian Sergey Diaghilev most closely associated?
4. Michelangelo completed his most famous work on a ceiling in Italy after four and a half years. Where is the ceiling and in what city?
5. Give the name of the sculptures and decorative architectural fragments which came from the Parthenon and other Athenian buildings and were brought to London by the Ambassador to Turkey in 1799.
6. Mechlin Lappet, Venetian rose-point, Genoese, Old Honiton and Modern Duchesse are all forms of what?
7. What was the name of the decorative style of the twenties and thirties which was characterised by geometric design and bright metallic surfaces?
8. Domenikos Theotocopolous was a notable artist in the 16th Century and lived in Spain painting for the Spanish Court. How was he better known?
9. The Statue of Liberty holds in her left hand a tablet bearing the date of the Declaration of Independence. What does she hold in her right hand?
10. Who was the famous dancer who was killed when her

long scarf was caught in the wheel of a motor-car in 1927?

11. In ballet, what does the term 'sur les pointes' mean?

12. In which art gallery would you find the *Venus de Milo*?

13. Which famous painter do you associate with the film *Moulin Rouge*?

14. Which master portraitist who lived from 1723–1792 was the first President of the Royal Academy?

15. What did Sir Joseph Paxton design for the Great Exhibition in Hyde Park, London, in 1851?

16. In which Belgian city could you visit the house of the great painter Rubens?

17. What is the name of the palace at Seville, famed for the beauty and splendour of its halls and gardens?

18. The Louvre in Paris, France, is now a famous museum and art gallery. What was it before it was used for this purpose?

19. Which art gallery in London is famous for its five Turner galleries?

20. Across which city does the statue of *Christ of Corcovado* look?

21. His name was Buonarroti and he lived between 1475 and 1564. He was a Florentine sculptor, architect and painter. By what name was he better known?

22. What name is used to describe a painting or sculpture of the Virgin Mary holding the body of the dead Christ?

23. The Italian painter Giotto is reputed to have proved his skill as an artist in a simple but remarkable way when presented to the Pope. What did he do?

24. What name is given to the twentieth century art form where the painting is inspired by the exploration of the sub-conscious?

25. Which colour in art signifies royalty?

26. From which country did the artist Velasquez come?

27. What is the name of the Spanish national museum of painting and sculpture in Madrid?

23

28. What is the name of the tapestry, designed by Graham Sutherland, which hangs in Coventry Cathedral?
29. In which field of the arts was the Englishwoman Barbara Hepworth a notable exponent?
30. In which field of the arts was Inigo Jones a notable exponent during the late 16th and early 17th centuries?
31. Oil paints are made by grinding dry pigments in oil. What kind of oil is generally used in this medium?
32. What name is given to the annual festival of the Arts in Wales?
33. What is the Japanese art-form of paper folding called?
34. Gamboge is a resinous gum which is used as a pigment in paint – what colour does it make?
35. Who was the architect who was chiefly responsible for the rebuilding of many of London's churches following their destruction in the Great Fire of London?
36. In which of the arts did Joan Sutherland achieve world-wide fame?
37. What is the art of topiary?
38. To which union do the majority of actors belong?
39. With which of the arts is the name Claudio Arrau associated?
40. What name is given to the Japanese art of arranging cut flowers into aesthetically pleasing designs?

Astronomy

1. What was the name of the American project to put a man on the moon?
2. What are commonly referred to as shooting stars?
3. Which planet has a great red spot?

4. By what other names are the constellations Corona Australis and Corona Borealis popularly known?
5. What name is given to the highest point in the heavens?
6. How many complete revolutions does the moon make around the earth in a calendar year?
7. By what other name is the constellation Pyxis known?
8. Which star constellation represents a hunter with his club and shield raised?
9. What name is given to the irregular rocky bodies which orbit the sun?
10. Which is the closest of the planets to the Sun and is never visible with the naked eye, except when close to the horizon?
11. What are Sirius, Vega, Rigel and Altair?
12. What is the meaning of the name of the constellation Capricornus?
13. Which planet in our solar system has two moons, one named Phobos and a smaller one named Demos?
14. Which planet was discovered by J G Galle in 1846?
15. What is the name of the radio observatory of the University of Manchester, near Macclesfield, Cheshire?
16. In astronomy, what is the 'big bang' theory?
17. Which is the largest of the nine planets which orbit the sun?
18. What is remarkable about the direction of a comet's tail?
19. What name is given to the phenomenon of the earth or moon entering the other's shadow?
20. Which sign of the zodiac is represented by the Virgin?
21. Who first advanced the argument, around 385–325 BC, that the world was not flat?
22. Which major constellation of the northern hemisphere represents a princess in Greek mythology?
23. Which star is also known as the North Star or Pole Star?
24. Between which two planets do almost all of the asteroids in our solar system orbit the sun?

25. Give another name for the star constellation known as The Great Bear?
26. John Flamstead was the first English Astronomer Royal. Which King constructed the Royal Observatory at Greenwich for him?
27. Neil Armstrong was the first man to set foot on the surface of the moon – but who was the second?
28. What famous hypothesis was put forward by Nicholas Copernicus in 1543?
29. The earth is approximately 7,900 miles in diameter. Which other planet in our solar system is similar in size, with a diameter of 7,519 miles?
30. What is the traditional sign of the zodiac for Gemini?
31. Which planet did Mariner 9 photograph in 1971–2?
32. Which is the nearest star to our sun?
33. Which sign of the zodiac follows Scorpio?
34. What do Hoba, Tent (Abnighito), Baruberito and Williamette have in common?
35. What are the Northern Lights otherwise known as?
36. How often does Halley's Comet orbit the sun?
37. What is the name of the largest moon of Jupiter?
38. What name is given to the faint band of starlight seen crossing the sky on clear, dark evenings?
39. Which is the third planet from the sun?
40. What is the name of the American space vehicle which in 1980 passed by Saturn and transmitted spectacular photographs of its rings and moons?
41. Which major planet was discovered in 1846?
42. Which constellation of the zodiac is represented by the water carrier?
43. Only one astrological sign is not named after a living creature – which one?
44. What name in astronomy is given to an area in space in which the pull of gravity is so strong that nothing can escape, not even light?

The Bible

1. According to Genesis, on the seventh day God rested. What did he do on the fourth day?
2. How many Chapters are there in the Old Testament Book of Numbers?
3. What kind of bird did Noah first release from the Ark after the rains abated?
4. To what was Jesus referring when he said: 'I say unto you that even Solomon in all his glory was not arrayed like one of these'?
5. How long was Jonah said to have spent in the belly of the whale?
6. What was the name of the angel sent by God to Mary to tell her she was to be the mother of Jesus?
7. Who was the villainous female in the Old Testament who was eaten by dogs?
8. Which hill marks the traditional site of the Ascension?
9. The authorized version of the Bible was published in 1611. Who authorized it?
10. Name the fifth book in the Old Testament.
11. What were the names of the three kings known as The Magi?
12. What was it, according to Genesis, that was constructed out of Gopher wood?
13. With which wood is King Solomon said to have panelled 'from floor to rafter' the interior of his temple at Jerusalem?
14. In the Garden of Eden story, what were Adam and Eve forbidden to eat?

15. Where, according to the Book of Exodus, did God appear to Moses and give him the Ten Commandments?

16. Who made the golden calf for the people to worship while Moses was receiving the Ten Commandments?

17. What was the name of the Philistine giant who was slain by David?

18. Which town in Turkey was the birthplace of St Paul?

19. Who was the second son of Adam and Eve and who was murdered by his brother?

20. Which book does the Old Testament end with which repeats God's promise of the coming of the Messiah?

21. In the Bible, who was the Queen who questioned the wisdom of Solomon?

22. According to the Bible, who was the first Christian martyr?

23. Who were the parents of John the Baptist?

24. How did Judas Iscariot betray Jesus in the Garden of Gethsemane?

25. Name the first five books of The Bible.

26. In the Bible, what name did the Book of St John give to the great battle in which the last conflict between Good and Evil is to be fought?

27. In the Old Testament, what was the name of the portable sanctuary, carried by the Jews in their wanderings from Egypt to Palestine, which contained the Ark of the Covenant?

28. Who were Daniel's three companions in the fiery furnace?

29. What was the name of the archangel referred to in the Book of Daniel as the guardian angel of Israel?

30. What did Salome receive as a reward from Herod for her dancing?

31. Which biblical character was found as a baby floating in a hastily contrived boat?

32. Who were the parents of Mary, the Blessed Virgin?

33. Who were the parents of the twin brothers Esau and Jacob?

34. To what town was St Paul travelling when he was blinded by a vision of the Lord?

35. In the Old Testament, what were the names of the cities which were destroyed by God because of their wickedness?

36. Which grandson of Methuselah had three sons (Shem, Ham and Japheth) at the age of 500?

37. What is the last word in the New Testament?

38. What, in the Bible, is referred to as The Pentateuch?

39. In the story about the loaves and fishes, how many fish did Jesus require to feed the five thousand?

40. What general name, from the Anglo-Saxon words meaning 'good tidings', is given to the first four books of the New Testament?

41. Which city fell after Joshua and his armies marched round its walls for seven days?

42. What connection does Mount Ararat in Turkey have with the Book of Genesis in the Bible?

43. According to Exodus, what is the first commandment?

44. According to the book of Genesis, Esau sold his birth-right to his brother Jacob. What did he receive in payment?

45. Who in the Bible was asked to interpret the writing on the wall?

46. According to the Bible, who was the father of the Jewish race?

47. Only one miracle is mentioned in all four Gospels – which one is it?

48. What kind of trees grew in the Garden of Gethsemane – the scene of Christ's agony and betrayal?

49. Who was the Roman administrator of Judea who pronounced the judgement on Jesus Christ and condemned him to death?

50. What, in the Bible, is known as the decalogue?

51. In which book of the bible can be found the story of the birth of Moses?

52. Which biblical character, according to the Book of Samuel, was born in Gath?

53. Simon, called Peter, with his brother, were both disciples and followers of Christ. What was his brother's name?
54. Who baptised Jesus Christ and in which river did the baptism take place?
55. According to Genesis, the twelve tribes of Israel are named after whose twelve sons?
56. What is the last book in the Bible?

Buildings

1. Which house in London used to be known as 'Number One London'?
2. St George's Chapel is found in which royal residence?
3. It is an ancient palace and fortress in Spain, in Grenada, famous for its fountains, nightingales and trees – what is its name?
4. Who designed The Cathedral Church of St Michael in Coventry, which was consecrated in May 1962?
5. What was the name of the City of London's first theatre for 300 years which was opened in 1959?
6. Gilbert Scott designed the Albert Memorial in London and was knighted for his work. In which park would you find this memorial?
7. What famous building would you find in the city of Agra?
8. In which English cathedral does a mechanical figure known as Jack Blandiver sound the quarter-hours with two hammers on a small suspended bell?
9. Can you name the largest Christian church in the world?
10. What is the high tower of a Moslem Mosque called?

11. Which buildings did Don Quixote mistake for evil giants?
12. Who was the English civil engineer responsible for the Clifton Suspension Bridge and the Royal Albert Bridge?
13. Name the Swiss architect responsible for the chapel of Notre Dame du Haut in Ronchamp?
14. Durham Cathedral has one of the most majestic examples of which type of architecture?
15. Who was the French administrator and planner who replanned the city centre of Paris between 1853 and 1868 and laid down the foundation of today's beautiful city?
16. What is the architectural term used to describe the central part of a church between the choir and the entrance?
17. He was an architect – one of four Scottish brothers – who developed a characteristic style in planning and decoration, including the design of Harewood House, Osterley Park, Syon House and Kenwood. Who was he?
18. In which building is the Lord Mayor's Banquet held?
19. What name was given to the towers built along the Sussex and Kent coasts in 1804 as a defence against the threatened French invasion?
20. Sears Tower is 110 storeys high. In which American city would you find this building?
21. What is a campanile?
22. What name is given to the style of church building in the period 1360–1540?
23. What type of bridge is the Tower Bridge in London?
24. In which English cathedral would you find a tower named Bell Harry?
25. An architectural structure was built in London and is known as the Monument. What does it commemorate?
26. Which feature of the cathedral of Chartres in France is famous?

27. Where would you find the 7 metre bronze statues of St Michael and the Devil by Sir Jacob Epstein?

28. In which English stately home would you find the Canaletto Room where 21 masterpieces by this great artist are hung?

29. The Triumphal Way, the Water Gardens and the Sunken Italian Gardens are famous features of which palace?

30. In architectural terms, what name is given to a low storey of a building between two higher ones?

31. What is the name of Edinburgh's cathedral?

32. Which former home of Madame de Pompadour became the official residence of the French President in 1873?

33. In which country would you find the 2,000-year-old aqueduct of Segovia with its spectacular 120 arches?

34. Name the largest Gothic church in northern Europe.

35. The Unknown Soldier of Italy is buried within the huge structure of the Vittorio Emanuele Monument. What is the nickname of this monument?

36. Name the British architect who was the designer of the Houses of Parliament, Westminster (1840–60).

37. What is the name of the official country home of the British Prime Minister, near Princes Risborough in Buckinghamshire?

38. Who was the French engineer who conceived the idea of the Suez Canal – completed in 1869?

39. George III bought it in 1762 and the architect John Nash rebuilt it in 1825. What is it?

40. Of which fine Yorkshire stately home did Horace Walpole say, 'I have seen gigantic palaces before, but never such a sublime one'?

41. What name is given to the part of a building where bells are hung?

42. Edward VI was born there; Mary and Elizabeth held court there; and Charles I lived there as a king and a condemned prisoner. Which palace is this?

43. Name the third largest cathedral in England after St

Paul's and York Minster.

44. Name the world's largest office building.
45. In which English city would you find the Cathedral of Christ the King which has a stained glass cylinder which culminates in 16 pinnacles which form a crown of thorns against the sky?
46. It was Charles II who founded the Royal Hospital, Chelsea, where the Chelsea Pensioners live. Who designed this building?
47. How many storeys has the Empire State Building in New York?
48. Where would you find the Mathematical Bridge, so named because it is allegedly constructed without using nails, based solely on geometrical principles?
49. Which building in London was christened the National Cruet Stand when it was built in 1838?

The Calendar

1. In which year is it traditional for a woman to make a proposal of marriage to the person she loves rather than waiting for the man to propose to her?
2. On which date is Burns Night celebrated?
3. On which day is Canada's Dominion Day or Canada Day celebrated?
4. In England, Wales and Northern Ireland, four days in the year are known as Quarter Days. Can you name these days?
5. Julius Caesar was murdered on the Ides of March, 44 BC. What date was this?
6. What name is given to the eve of All Saints' Day?
7. On which date is the anniversary of the revolution celebrated in Russia?

33

8. Which date is known in Britain as Poppy Day – a day of remembrance, in honour of the men and women killed during war?

9. On which date does International Labour Day fall?

10. February 6th, Waitangi Day, is the national day in which country?

11. Which Saint's day falls on March 1st?

12. Which famous competition is held on Good Friday at Tinsley Green, Sussex?

13. In which countries is Anzac Day (celebrated on 25th April) an important anniversary?

14. What is celebrated on the fourth Thursday in November in America and is a national holiday?

15. At which time of the year would you be most likely to hear the song *Ding, Dong, Merrily on High*?

16. Which month of the year is derived from the Roman god of war?

17. What are the dates of the shooting season for pheasant?

18. Legend says that if it rains on St Swithin's Day, it will rain for forty days afterwards. What is the date of St Swithin's Day?

19. On which day is the action of first-footing carried out?

20. In which month does the State Opening of Parliament normally take place?

21. When is American Independence Day?

22. What other name is given to Twelfth Night?

23. Which month of the year derived its name from Julius Caesar?

24. What are the names given to the old and new styles of calendar?

25. When does the oyster season begin?

Cartoon Characters

1. One of Bambi's friends was called Thumper. What type of animal was Thumper?
2. In *Sleeping Beauty* what were the names of Princess Aurora's three fairy godmothers?
3. What type of animal was the friendly Thomas O'Malley?
4. Dewey, Huey and Louie were the nephews of which famous Disney character?
5. What was the name of the animal who sang *Zip-a-dee-Doo-dah* in Walt Disney's adaption of Joel Chandler Harris's *Tales of Uncle Remus*?
6. What was the name of the cartoon cat who constantly tried to eat the canary called Tweety Pie?
7. What was the name of the Disney elephant with jumbo-sized ears?
8. Name the cartoon character who was 'the fastest mouse in all Mehico'.
9. Musky Muskrat was the sidekick of which cartoon lawman?
10. Who was the big brown bear who protected Mowgli in Walt Disney's *The Jungle Book*?
11. What type of animal was J Worthington Foul Fellow?
12. Where was the home of Fred Flinstone?
13. What were the names of the Seven Dwarfs in Disney's first full feature length cartoon, *Snow White and the Seven Dwarfs*?
14. Name the beagle in the *Peanuts* comic strip.
15. Who was Popeye's chief opponent who tried to woo Olive Oyl away from her spinach-eating boyfriend?

16. Which cartoon character was featured in the short film *Steamboat Willie*?
17. Dumbo the elephant made friends with a mouse. What was the name of this mouse?
18. Who created the popular 1920s cartoon character Felix the Cat?
19. Who is the hero of the Snoopy cartoons created by Charles M Schulz?
20. What is the name of the calculating fat cat created by Jim Davis in his comic strips?

Common Link

1. What do the following have in common: Girton, Newnham and New Hall?
2. What did Maskelyne, Chung Ling Soo and Servais Le Roy have in common?
3. Leap-Frog, The Gallant Hussar and Ampleforth are all types of what?
4. What are known by the names Oxford Treble Bob, Bob Major and Grandsire Triple?
5. Escritoire, flap-and-tambour, military and kneehole are all types of what?
6. James Baines, Thermopylae, Ariel and Taeping were all what type of conveyance?
7. Charles Dickens, John Pounds and Isambard Brunel were all born in which city?
8. Byzantine, Romanesque, Baroque and Brutalism are all what?
9. What do maiden, mother-of-all and footman have in common?
10. What did Flamsteed, Halley, Bradley and Bliss have in common?

11. What do Wyandotte, Buff Orpington and Rhode Island Red have in common?
12. What do a brandy puncheon, butt, hogshead and kilderkin have in common?
13. What do Blackwall, Rotherhithe and Dartford have in common?
14. Lord Byron, R B Sheridan, Sir Robert Peel, Lord Palmerston and Sir Winston Churchill all attended which public school?
15. What are Auk, Montrose, Piper and Beryl?
16. Deveraux, Flint, Bell, Wakefield, Cradle, Bloody, Brick and Martin all have something in common. What is it?
17. What do Pelmanism, Beggar My Neighbour, Miss Milligan and Racing Demons have in common?
18. What personal characteristic did the Monarchs James I, George IV and Queen Victoria have in common?
19. What do Paddy McCready, Elizabeth of Glamis and Dorothy Perkins have in common?
20. What do pinto, borlotti, cannellini and kidney have in common?
21. What do the tomb of St James of Compostella in Spain, the shrine of Becket in Canterbury and Lourdes in France have in common?
22. What do Swallowtail, The Scottish Angus and The Camberwell have in common?
23. What did James Keir Hardie, Bertrand Russell and Gandhi have in common?
24. What did Mary Queen of Scots, Marie Antoinette and Annie Oakley have in common?
25. What do emus, cassowaries and kiwis have in common?
26. What do Scarlet Pimpernel, James Grieve and Egremont Russett have in common?
27. What do Fairbourne, Snowdon Mountain and Leighton Buzzard have in common?
28. What do Brahmans, Kshatriyas, Vaisyas and Shudras have in common?

29. What did Jonn S Copley, Benjamin West, Winslow Homer and Jackson Pollock have in common?
30. What did Jock Sutherland, Gregory Brandon, Jack Ketch and Thomas Cheshire have in common?
31. What do Football, Woolworth, Heinz and Dr Pepper have in common?
32. What do Karl Marx, Michael Faraday, Herbert Spencer and George Eliot have in common?
33. What do Romney Marsh, Suffolk, Clun, Forest and Swaledale have in common?
34. What do tulip, balloon, and flute have in common?
35. What did the poets Wordsworth, Tennyson, John Masefield and John Betjeman have in common?
36. What do nitrous oxide, sodium pentothal and cyclopropane have in common?
37. What do Micmac, Cree and Ojibwa have in common?
38. What do Coburg, Vienna, Cottage and Bloomer have in common?
39. Clout, Lost Head, Box and French are all types of what?
40. What do Glastonbury, Caquetoire and an Elizabeth X have in common?

Crime & Punishment

1. Richard John Bingham disappeared after the alleged murder of a nanny in London. By what title is he better known?
2. Which criminal's arrest made history as it was the first time that wireless telegraphy had been used for police purposes?
3. For whose death was James Earl Ray responsible in 1968?

4. Alfred Dreyfus was a Frenchman falsely accused of treason and sent to a notorious penal colony from which few escaped or survived – what was the name of this infamous prison?
5. Which famous criminal lived at 10 Rillington Place?
6. How did Ruth Ellis become famous in British criminal history in 1955?
7. Fleet Prison stood on the east side of Farringdon Street, in London. For what was it particularly known?
8. What name is given to the crime of deliberately burning someone else's property?
9. Bastinado was an eastern form of punishment. Of what did it consist?
10. Daniel Defoe and Fielding both wrote about the notorious character Jonathan Wilde who was hanged in 1725. What activity led to his notoriety?
11. Which criminal was known as Scarface?
12. Who was the man known as the Brides in the Bath Murderer? He was condemned to death in 1915 for his murder of Beatrice Mundy, Alice Burnham and Margaret Lofty.
13. What type of person may have been referred to as a cutpurse?
14. Why was Hare released following the trial of his fellow criminal Burke in the infamous body-snatchers case in Edingurgh?
15. He was the hero of a mythical ride from London to York in Ainsworth's novel *Rookwood*. He was hanged in York aged 33. Who was he?
16. Who was the burglar and murderer who used his violin case for carrying his burgling tools? He was sentenced to death in 1878.
17. By what nickname was the criminal Albert De Salvo better known?
18. Name the infamous maximum security prison (now disused) which was situated on an island in the middle of San Francisco Bay?

19. Who was known as The Demon Barber of Fleet Street?
20. What was the popular nickname given to the unknown murderer of eight prostitutes in the east end of London during 1887–9?
21. Who, according to tradition, murdered several wives in turn because they showed undue curiosity about a locked room?
22. What was named the 'crime of the century' in 1963?
23. The pillory was a device used for punishing wrongdoers. Which parts of the body were held in the pillory?
24. What was the name of the former nurse who was convicted at Durham for poisoning a stepson and who was suspected of committing another 15 murders for petty gains, who was hanged in March 1873?
25. Where are the headquarters of the Metropolitan Police in London?
26. Who was charged with firing the shot from the Texas Book Depository Building in Dallas on 22nd November 1963, which killed President J F Kennedy?
27. What was the name of the first penal colony established by the British Government in New South Wales in 1788?
28. What is the crime when a person deceives someone else so that he gives up his property or another legal right?
29. John George Haigh was hanged for murder in August 1949. What ingenious method did he use to get rid of his victims' bodies?
30. The police chief Alphonse Bertillon is often credited with the invention of the finger-print method of detection, yet this was largely the work of whom?
31. What was the name of the judge who presided over the courts known as the Bloody Assizes?
32. The figure of justice on the Old Bailey in London holds a set of scales in one hand. What is in the other hand?

33. Socrates, the Greek philosopher, was sentenced to death. How was the sentence carried out?
34. Who shot Ronald Reagan in March 1981?
35. In which year (to the nearest three years) was the last judicial hanging in Great Britain?
36. The Bow Street Runners were a group of men paid to prevent crimes and riots, prior to a police force in Britain. Which novelist started this group in 1750?
37. Who was the 17th century English adventurer who almost succeeded in stealing the Crown Jewels?

Decorations & Emblems

1. What is the highest decoration awarded for bravery to civilians in the United Kingdom?
2. What is the name of the flag of the French Republic?
3. What is the name of the oldest military award in the USA which was instituted by George Washington in 1782?
4. The Union Jack is flown at half mast for three occasions, what are they?
5. What is the inscription on the obverse side of the Victoria Cross?
6. What is the national emblem which appears on the Canadian flag?
7. If a staff with a coiled serpent symbolizes medicine, what is said to symbolize education?
8. What does it mean if the Union Jack is flown upside down from a ship or building?
9. The flag of Nepal is unique in terms of national flags. What is remarkable about it?
10. Which two colours make up the Polish flag?

11. What colour ribbon has the Victoria Cross?
12. How many points has a Star of David?
13. A statue called The Spirit of Ecstasy is internationally famous and may be seen in many of the more affluent countries of the world – why?
14. If a heraldic figure or beast is described as couchant, what would it be doing?
15. In Britain there are four orders of knighthood. What are they?
16. How many lobes or sets of petals does a tudor rose have?
17. Who wears a signet ring that is sometimes called The Fisherman's Ring?
18. The Union Jack consists of three heraldic crosses. Can you name them?
19. Of what is the bluebird a symbol?
20. Which German military decoration consists of a Maltese cross of iron, edged with silver?
21. What are the colours of the flag of the United Nations?
22. What is the title of the Chief Herald in Scotland?
23. The maple leaf is the botanical emblem of Canada and the thistle is the botanical emblem of Scotland. What is the botanical emblem of Australia?
24. The flag of which country can be described as follows: a Union Jack in the top left-hand corner, with four stars on a blue background?
25. Which national flag – a white cross set against a red background – was adopted in 1219?
26. What name is given to the ceremony of conferring a knighthood where the sovereign touches the knight lightly on each shoulder with the flat of a sword?
27. What is the name of the British Order of Merit awarded to members of the Army, Navy and Air Force for conspicuous valour? It was established in 1856.
28. What is known as 'the Stars and Stripes'?
29. Which flag is red with a five-pointed yellow star at its centre?
30. What is a Jolly Roger?

Dress

1. Which Mary was the British dress and fashion designer who revolutionized the world of clothes, jewellery, cosmetics and fashion in the sixties?
2. What colour sari is traditionally worn by an Indian bride at her wedding?
3. A fashionable Country Club at a park in New York gave its name to a dinner jacket or evening dress for men. Name it.
4. Where would you wear espadrilles?
5. Name the long, loose, coarse over-garment, prescribed by law as the distinctive garment of the Jews in the Middle Ages (as worn by Shylock).
6. In which country might the soldiers wear a stiff white kilt known as a fustanella?
7. Who would be seen wearing a trousseau?
8. Smocking is a popular form of decoration on young children's clothing. What is the name of the stitch in which smocking is worked?
9. Which item of clothing did James Belcher give his name to in the nineteenth century?
10. A dolly varden is an article of clothing – what kind?
11. A male's formal evening dress-coat is often referred to as 'tails'. Why is this?
12. What article of dress or clothing comes in the following forms: Domino, Cardinal, Pelegrine, Mantle, Dolman and Inverness?
13. Which item of dress was launched in the sixties by Mr Fish, a fashion entrepreneur?
14. What name is given to the thin veil worn by Moslem women in public?

15. If you were wearing a Sam Brown what would you have on?

16. What name was given to the embroidered box-like contraption at the front of men's breeches in the early sixteenth century?

17. Sir Anthony Eden gave his name to which item of dress, popularized by him in the thirties?

18. What was the name of the very narrow skirt introduced in 1910, which made it difficult for the wearer to walk?

19. An anorak is a long hooded jacket of skin or cloth but from what language does the word anorak come?

20. Which Paris couturier introduced the New Look in 1947?

21. Who would wear an Orphrey, Morse and Cope and carry a crozier?

22. Which everyday French word is used to describe the long waterproof outer garment with a hood, which is often worn by hillwalkers?

23. An Aran Knit sweater is a popular and well-known type of patterned knitwear – but where are the Aran Islands from which the name comes?

24. What is the name given to the tweed cloth made in the Scottish Highlands of the Outer Hebrides?

25. What is the name given to the lace scarf worn over the head and shoulders by Spanish women?

26. Which article of clothing was referred to as a homburg?

27. What was the nickname of the French fashion designer Gabrielle Chanel?

28. The frills on a man's dress-shirt front have the same name as the small intestine of animals prepared for food. What is this name?

29. Which article of clothing, worn by British soldiers during the Crimean War, was named after the Earl who commanded the Light Brigade at Balaclava?

30. Who would have worn a gorget, pauldron, beaver and greave?

31. What is the name of the colour of the clothing supposedly worn by Robin Hood and his men, to match the forest in which they hid?
32. What name is given to a type of cloak, originating in South America, which resembles a blanket with a central hole for the head?
33. What is the name of the kind of pouch which Scotsmen wear in front of their kilts?
34. What is the name of women's trousers which are made to look like a skirt?
35. What is the name of the top fashion designer nicknamed Punk Princess of Fashion?
36. Name the English couturier who designed the wedding and coronation dresses of Queen Elizabeth II.
37. What were known as Oxford Bags?
38. On what part of the body is a wimple worn and who would normally be seen wearing it?

Exploration & Discovery

1. Who was the English naturalist who accompanied Cook on his expedition around the world and was the leading figure in the development of Kew Gardens?
2. What was the name of the legendary city of gold which inspired the Spanish conquest of South and Central America?
3. Who was the first man to fly the Atlantic solo?
4. Who is reputed to have commanded the first Viking ship across the North Atlantic to Newfoundland?
5. What names were given to the first Russian and first American satellites in the conquest of space?
6. Which European Prince was known as The Navigator?
7. In which country was the explorer H M Stanley born?

8. Which British navigator and explorer gave his name to a city and island off the West coast of North America?

9. Sinbad the sailor set out on a voyage of exploration over 2000 years ago. Where did he go?

10. It was formerly called the Cape of Storms by early explorers but was subsequently renamed with a more optimistic title. What is it now known as?

11. What was it that a gold prospector, named Jimmy Angel, discovered in the jungles of Venezuela in South America, that eventually found its way into the record books of natural phenomena?

12. Which early explorer died in the Philippines in 1521 whilst attempting a circumnavigation of the world?

13. Who was the American explorer who first reached the North Pole with Eskimo companions in 1909?

14. What was the name of the first communication satellite in orbit with the earth? It became a global carrier of TV programmes in May 1965?

15. Yuri Gagarin was the first man in space on 12 April 1961. What was the name of his space capsule?

16. In the honours list of explorers, who was the Italian who is usually given credit for discovering Newfoundland?

17. Thor Heyerdahl's first strange craft was named *Kontiki*, his second craft was named *Ra*. What was the name of his third craft in which he sailed up the coast of East Africa?

18. What were the names of the two explorers and surveyors who in 1763–67 surveyed a boundary which formed the division between the slave-owning states and the free states of America?

19. Who was the American polar explorer who was the first person to fly over both the North and South Poles and across the Atlantic Ocean?

20. Captain Cook discovered and named the Sandwich Islands but their name was subsequently changed to what?

21. What nationality was Christopher Columbus?
22. Who was the American explorer and film producer who made the first full-length documentary film *Nanook of the North* (1920)?
23. Who completed the first non-stop flight across the Atlantic on 15 June 1919?
24. In 1983 the USA launched its first woman astronaut. What was her name?
25. Who was the Italian merchant explorer whose name was given to the Continent of America?
26. Which great Victorian traveller was the first Westerner to penetrate the holy Muslim city of Mecca and the first white man to sail down the Amazon?
27. Francis Chichester rounded Cape Horn in 1967 during a single-handed voyage around the world. What was the name of the second Englishman who also rounded the Cape alone in his yacht *Lively Lady*?
28. Who was the US Space Shuttle captain of Challenger who in 1984 became the first astronaut to 'walk' in space without a safety line?
29. Who led the first exploration team to reach the South Pole and what was his nationality?
30. What did the British explorers John Speke and James Grant discover in 1862 which resolved a centuries-long mystery?
31. What was the nationality of the explorer Mungo Park who pioneered exploration of the River Niger?
32. What is the name of the United States' project for manned exploration of the moon?
33. Who was the Frenchman who discovered the St Lawrence River?
34. Which Scottish explorer discovered the course of the Zambesi, the Victoria Falls and Lake Nyasa?

Famous People : General

1. Which great woman scientist was awarded two Nobel Prizes in the early years of the twentieth century?
2. Born in 1835, this son of a poor Scottish weaver became an American multi-millionaire. He gave most of his money away to benefit the public, notably by founding libraries. Who was he?
3. Who organised the first Continental holiday tour in 1855?
4. What did the Polish oculist Dr L L Zamenhof invent?
5. John Metcalf was an English engineer who devised new and improved methods of road-making and bridge-building, but what physical handicap did he suffer all his life?
6. Who, according to legend, was the son of Uther Pendragon, became King of Britain at the age of 15, held court at Caerleon and was mortally wounded at the Battle of Camelford?
7. Name the great English landscape gardener who designed the grounds of Blenheim Palace and transformed the landscape of extensive areas of the United Kingdom during the 18th Century.
8. He was a friend of the Prince Regent in the early 1800s and his fashionable and sometimes extravagant dress led to his name being used as a byword for elegance – who was he?
9. For what is Francis Scott Key best remembered by Americans?
10. He was a chemist and micro-biologist and one of the greatest scientists of the nineteenth century. He

showed the connection between germs and disease and developed vaccines for rabies, anthrax and cholera. Who was he?

11. Name the English mathematician who devised a mechanical calculating machine in 1834 which was the fore-runner of modern computers.

12. With what do you associate the names of Mary Read and Anne Bonny, who lived during the eighteenth century?

13. She was an English heroine who, with her father, rescued the crew of the ship *Forfarshire* which was wrecked on the Farne Islands on the north-east coast of England in 1838. Who was she?

14. What was Casanova's occupation at the time of his death?

15. What was the name of the Hunchback of Notre Dame?

16. Which broadcaster, who died in 1985, is most remembered for presenting Desert Island Discs?

17. Who was the leading Confederate General in the American Civil War who was accidentally shot by his own men at the Battle of Chancellorsville?

18. John Hurt achieved acclaim for his portrayal of a person labelled The Elephant Man. What was this man's real name?

19. Who was the South African financier of English descent who was the ruling spirit of the British South Africa Company? He had a country named after him.

20. The founder of a world-wide chain of department stores was born on 13 April 1852. Name him.

21. Who was the deaf and blind American authoress who wrote such works as *The Story of my Life*, *Out of the Dark* and *Let us have Faith*?

22. Who was the first and only Englishman ever to become Pope?

23. Who was one of the first women to enter the medical profession and was also the first female Mayor in her native town of Aldeburgh?

24. Who was the English financier who gave his name to the law that *bad* money tends to drive *good* money from circulation?

25. Which famous singer was assassinated in New York City in December 1980?

26. Who instituted the flat-rate penny post in England?

27. For what was Marie Montessori famous?

28. Name the 13-year-old who hit the headlines in 1985 when she gained a first-class honours degree in mathematics from Oxford University.

29. Who was The Maid of Orleans?

30. He was born in 1856 and died in 1939. He was an Austrian by birth and specialised in psychoanalysis. Who was he?

31. Robert the Bruce was a great Scottish hero. From which disease did he die in 1329?

32. Who was the famous French seer, or prophet, who lived between 1503 and 1566, yet predicted the Great Fire of London, the coming of Louis Pasteur, General Franco and the Civil War in Spain and – most remarkably – that an Austrian named Hister (Hitler) would lead Germany in a Great War but would eventually be defeated?

33. Who was the American businessman who founded the first large department store in Britain in 1909?

34. Which woman, dedicated to the relief of the poor, won the 1979 Nobel Peace Prize?

35. Who led the Chinese forces against the Japanese during World War II?

36. Who was the Quaker who lived in Norwich who was an active reformer of English prisons in the nine-teenth century?

37. Which Frenchman's work for the blind earned him the title Father and Apostle of the Blind?

38. Who was the young Scotswoman who risked her life to save Prince Charles Edward Stuart after his defeat at the hands of the Duke of Cumberland?

39. In 1934, who became the first woman general of the

entire Salvation Army?

40. To which Highland clan did the Scottish outlaw Rob Roy belong?

41. Whom did Mehmet Ali Aga attempt to assassinate on 13th May 1981?

42. Who, when handed the insignia of the Order of Merit on her deathbed, said, 'Too kind – too kind'?

43. Who was the BBC's principal television commentator during the coronation of Queen Elizabeth II?

44. What was the name of the English headmaster whose influence at Rugby School (1828–42) gave it a renowned position among public schools?

45. Who was the daughter of the Indian Chief Powhatan who saved the life of Captain John Smith and was later baptised as Rebecca?

46. Who abolished St Valentine's Day, Hogmanay and Halloween as being altogether too frivolous and irreligious?

47. Alexander Graham Bell is known for his invention of the telephone. What was his profession?

48. Which British economist is famous for his *Essay on the Principle of Population* in which he maintained that while the population increases in geometrical ratio, food supply increases in arithmetical ratio?

Famous People :
The World Of Politics

1. What was the name of the Cuban President overthrown by Fidel Castro in 1959?

2. For what was Nancy Astor famous?

3. Mahatma Gandhi qualified in England for which profession before practising in South Africa?
4. Who was the American Negro leader who was assassinated at Memphis, Tennessee, in 1968?
5. He was brought up in Scotland where he worked in the mines by day and studied by night. He was an energetic union worker and formed the Scottish Labour Party in 1889. He became the first independent Labour MP in Britain. Who was he?
6. What was the name of the suffragette who threw herself in front of King George V's horse during The Derby in 1913?
7. George Washington was the first American President of the United States of America. Who was the second?
8. Who was known as the Welsh Wizard?
9. What was the name of the dictator of Haiti (1957–71), who was known as Papa Doc?
10. Which leader's statue was pulled down from its place in Red Square in 1991?
11. Who was in office as President of the United States when the decision was taken to declare war on Germany during World War I?
12. Who was the architect of the British National Health Service?
13. Who was hailed as the founder of the Mongol Empire?
14. Which Canadian newspaper magnate held important Government Offices in England during World War I and World War II?
15. Josip Broz led the Communist partisans to victory against foreign occupation forces in Yugoslavia during the Second World War. By what name was he later better known?
16. Which British statesman led his party to victory in the 1959 elections on the slogan 'You have never had it so good'?
17. Who, at the age of forty-three, became the world's

first female President and the youngest Head of State in Latin America in the seventies?

18. Who was Minister of Labour 1929–31 and the first woman to enter the Cabinet and be a member of the Privy Council?

19. Who was the 18th century Irish politician who was called 'the Liberator'?

20. Which former American President left behind an immortal souvenir – the teddy – which was named after him?

21. Which two men were awarded the Nobel Peace Price in 1993?

22. She was the leader of the British movement for female suffrage. In 1903 she founded the Women's Political Union which agitated for votes for women, but died in 1928 just before full voting rights were granted. Who was she?

23. He was Emperor of Ethiopia from 1930 until his dethronement in 1974, with the exception of 1936–41 (the Italian occupation). He was a founder of the Organisation of African Unity. Who was he?

24. Who was the President of the NUM at the time of the strikes in the 1980s?

25. He was born in Poland and emigrated to Palestine in 1906. He became the first Prime Minister of the State of Israel. Who was he?

26. Who was known as the Iron Chancellor?

27. A Norwegian politician became a puppet leader of his country during World War II and his name became a byword for treachery. Who was he?

28. What were the early occupations of the Italian dictator Benito Mussolini?

29. He was the son of a Siberian peasant and became the most influential person at the court of Tsar Nicholas II. The Tsarina thought him a divinely sent figure who would save Russia. He was widely thought to have magical powers and was assassinated in 1916. What was his name?

30. Who was the Prime Minister of Great Britain when Edward VIII abdicated the throne in 1936?

31. Who was known by the nickname The Great Commoner?

32. Ceylon (now Sri Lanka) had the first woman head of government. Who was she?

33. Which wife of a politician said in 1981, 'Woman is like a teabag: you can't tell how strong she is until you put her in the hot water'?

34. Which leader of the Russian revolution became first Soviet Commissar for Foreign Affairs but was expelled from the Communist Party in 1927 and was assassinated in Mexico in 1940?

35. Who was assassinated whilst sailing from the village of Mullaghmore in Ireland in 1979?

36. What was the name of the woman who married Adolph Hitler shortly before they both committed suicide?

37. The 25th President of the USA had the highest peak in North America named after him. Can you name him?

38. He was a Spanish hero who, before he was 20, led a Spanish force against the Moors and drove them out of Spain. He is celebrated in poem and romance. Who was he?

39. Ernesto 'Che' Guevara, the revolutionary hero, took part in guerilla wars in Cuba and was killed fighting Bolivian troops, but what nationality was he?

40. Who became Prime Minister of Great Britain when he was only twenty-four years old, the youngest person ever to be offered this post?

41. Who was elected the first woman Lord Mayor of London in September 1983?

42. Which British Prime Minister worked as a research chemist in industry before becoming a Member of Parliament in 1959?

Films : Actors

1. Which actor with the nasty guy image starred in *Marty, The Dirty Dozen* and *Convoy*?

2. Which American actor who starred in *One Flew Over The Cuckoo's Nest* and *Witches of Eastwick* stole the show with his 'comic' role in *Batman*?

3. Which actor of the television series *Fawlty Towers* and member of the Monty Python team went on to star in the film *A Fish Called Wanda*?

4. Who was the American film actor who starred in the film *Bullit*?

5. Which British film actor was known for his roles in the 1930s films *The Private Life of Henry VIII* and *Mutiny on the Bounty*?

6. Which star of the screen had his feet insured for $150,000?

7. Which actor-comedian married Anne Howe, Britt Ekland, Miranda Quarry and Lynne Frederick?

8. Name the British actor whose films include *The Long Good Friday, Mona Lisa, Who Framed Roger Rabbit*? and *Mermaids*.

9. Which American comedian's last words in 1959 were 'That was the best icecream soda I ever tasted'?

10. Which actor starred in *Our Man Flint, Waterhole Three* and *Cross of Iron*?

11. The most decorated American soldier in the Second World War became a famous film star. Who was he?

12. Which actor/singer was nearly eighty years of age when he made his final film *Monkeys Go Home* in 1967? (He died in Paris in 1972.)

13. Which British actor's films include *A Town Like Alice, The Pumpkin Eater* and *Sunday, Bloody Sunday*?

14. Which ex-Beatle starred in the 1967 anti-war film *How I Won The War*?

15. Which actor starred in *F.I.S.T., Paradise Alley* and *First Blood*?

16. Name the British actor who was in the following films: *The Elephant Man, Silence of the Lambs* and *The Remains of the Day*.

17. Which Canadian actor's films included *How Green Was My Valley, Mrs Miniver* and *Weekend at the Waldorf*?

18. Who was the male star of the following films of the 1920s: *Blood and Sand, The Eagle* and *Son of the Sheik*?

19. Which actor became a star in *Public Enemy* in 1931 and was still going strong in 1981 as a police commissioner in Milos Forman's film *Ragtime*?

20. Which film star do you associate with the saying 'Here's another fine mess you've gotten me into'?

21. Who, at the age of 80, became a box-office smash when he played God to John Denver in *Oh, God!*?

22. Which actor starred in *Downhill Racer, The Candidate* and *The Great Gatsby*?

23. What was Harold Lloyd's trademark?

24. Who, in the first talking picture, said, 'You ain't heard nothin' yet folks'?

25. Which American folk singer starred in the 1970 film *Gunfight*?

26. Which British character actor who died in 1979 aged 52, made his film debut in *The Dam Busters* (1955)?

27. Which film star is associated with the phrase 'Here's lookin' at you, kid'?

28. *Tom Jones, Charlie Bubbles* and *Annie* are all films starring which British actor?

29. He made his film debut in 1969 in *The Graduate* and starred in *Midnight Cowboy* and *Kramer vs Kramer* amongst many other fine films. Name him.

30. In the 1985 Oscars, who gained an honorary Oscar for 50 years of memorable performances?

Films : Actresses

1. Judy Garland's daughter became a famous film actress and singer. Name her.
2. Which actress was married and divorced from Artie Shaw, Mickey Rooney and Frank Sinatra?
3. Which number one pin-up girl of World War II starred in the 1940s films *Tin Pan Alley, Moon Over Miami* and *Springtime In The Rockies*?
4. Who played the heroine in the 1933 film *King Kong*?
5. Which actress returned to the big screen in 1985, after an absence of 14 years, in the film *The Assam Garden* which was filmed in South Wales?
6. In which film did Elizabeth Taylor become recognised as a child star in 1944?
7. Who became an international star in 1969 in the title role of *Anne of the Thousand Days*?
8. At 13 this actress won a BAFTA award for her role as a spoof 'siren' in *Bugsy Malone* and in 1988 she won Best Actress Oscar for *The Accused*. Name her.
9. Who won an Oscar for her portrayal of *Mrs Miniver* (1942) and became known as the Queen of MGM?
10. Which actress played the writer Lillian Hellman in Fred Zinnemann's film *Julia*?
11. Who became an overnight sex symbol when she made the film *10*?
12. Who was the Scottish born ballet dancer who came to films for the leading role in *The Red Shoes*?
13. Who was once described as 'an outrageous female impersonator' and starred in the films *Klondike Annie*

and *The Heat's On*?

14. Which German film star said, 'The relationship between the make-up man and the film actor is one of accomplices in crime'?

15. Which swimmer starred in *Bathing Beauty* and *Million Dollar Mermaid?*.

16. She was probably the greatest box office attraction of all time and yet she failed a test for the 'Our Gang' series. Who was she?

17. Which actress won Oscars for her unpleasant mother roles in *The Diary of Anne Frank* and *A Patch of Blue*?

18. Which actress's story was portrayed in the 1983 film *Mommie Dearest*?

19. Which classic movie star appeared in *Anna Christie, Queen Christina* and *Anna Karenina* in the 1930s?

20. Who is credited with the following memorable quotation: 'I never hated a man long enough to give him back his diamonds'?

Films :
Books & Autobiographies

1. Which film, starring Robert Redford and Mia Farrow, was based on a book by F Scott Fitzgerald?

2. Which actor's autobiography of 1978 was entitled *Dear Me*?

3. Which actress wrote a book on her well-publicised visit to the Republic of China called *You Can Get There From Here*?

4. Which actor who starred in the films *The Great Race* and *The Last Tycoon* published the novel *Kid Andrew Cooly and Julie Sparrow*?

5. Which actress's life is the subject of the adaptation of Terry Johnson's play *Insignificance*?

6. Which American actor's autobiography of 1953 was entitled *Call Me Lucky*?

7. Which film, which starred the pop star David Bowie, was based on the novel *The Seed and the Sower* by Laurens van der Post?

8. Cornelius Ryan's famous book *A Bridge Too Far* which was later made into a film was based on which famous battle?

9. Whose autobiographical books include *I Owe Russia $2,000* (1963), *The Last Christmas Show* (1976) and *The Road to Hollywood* (1977)?

10. The first Lassie film was *Lassie Come Home* in 1942. On whose novel was this film based?

11. Which young film sex symbol had the book *On Your Own* published in 1985?

12. Who wrote the book on which the film *The Stepford Wives* was based?

13. Which modern movie star published his autobiography in three parts called *A Postillion Struck By Lightning, Snakes and Ladders* and *Orderly Man*?

14. On whose novel was the film *Witness for the Prosecution* based?

15. Which actor's autobiography is called *Jack Of All Trades*?

Films : Characters/Roles

1. Tracy Lord, C K Dexter Haven and Macaulay Connor were all characters in which famous forties comedy?

2. Which actor stormed to stardom in 1964 as the lethal *Man With No Name*?

3. Which role did Michael Caine play in the film *The Ipcress File*?

4. Who starred opposite Madonna in the title role of the film *Dick Tracy*?

5. In the 1980s film *1984*, adapted from George Orwell's novel, who played the anti-hero Winston Smith and his tireless interrogator O'Brien?

6. Humphrey Bogart, Robert Montgomery, Dick Powell and James Garner have all played which private eye on film?

7. One of the earliest film roles of Tarzan was played by a famous American Olympic swimmer. What was his name?

8. Who played the literary tutor and his student in the 1983 film *Educating Rita*?

9. Which villain in the Bond films has been played by Telly Savalas, Charles Gray and Donald Pleasence?

10. *Stage Coach* was the film in which John Wayne played his first leading role. What character did he portray?

11. Which actors played the 'Woodstein' team responsible for uncovering Watergate in *All the President's Men*?

12. The film *High Noon* is generally regarded as one of the classic westerns of all time. Who played the role of Sheriff?

13. Who played the part of Inspector Clouseau in the *Pink Panther* films?

14. Which queen was personified on screen in the films *The Scarlet Empress* (1934), *A Royal Scandal* (1945) and *John Paul Jones* (1959)?

15. Who was the master criminal who gave Clark Kent his ultimate challenge in *Superman The Movie*?

16. Who starred as Zeus in the 1981 film *Clash of the Titans*?

17. Who played the part of Jack Somersby in the 1993 film *Somersby*?

18. What did Mary Kornman, Joe Cobb, Mickey Daniels and Jackie Condon have in common?

19. Who played the title role in the film *Blade Runner*?
20. Who played the tough, tired officer Murphy in *Fort Apache, The Bronx*?
21. Which Australian actor played the title role in the *Mad Max* series of films?
22. Who played Trotsky in the 1970s film *The Assassination of Trotsky*?
23. Who played the title role in the 1980 film *Brubaker*?
24. Who played a young idealistic lawyer in the 1980s film *And Justice For All*?
25. Who, in the world of films and novels, is known simply as 'M'?
26. Who played the Sheriff of Nottingham to Kevin Costner's Robin Hood in the film *Robin Hood, Prince of Thieves*?
27. In which film did the character R2D2 first appear?
28. In which cartoon film do the characters Frodo, Sam Gamgee, Merry, Pippin and Bilbo Baggins appear and what are they?

Films : Directors

1. Which American comedian wrote, directed and starred in the silent movies entitled *The Navigator* and *The General*?
2. Name the Czechoslovakian film director who became famous for *One Flew Over The Cuckoo's Nest*.
3. Who directed the film *Psycho*?
4. Who directed himself in *Sharky's Machine*?
5. Which American film-maker produced, directed and starred in the film *Citizen Kane* and produced, in 1938, a radio version of H G Wells's novel *War of the Worlds*?

6. Who was the Austrian-American film director who directed *Lost Weekend* (1945), *Sunset Boulevard* (1950) and *The Apartment* (1960)?
7. Which director won an Oscar in 1982 for his lengthy film about the young Indian advocate who became a quiet revolutionary, hailed as a saint and martyr?
8. Which American film director was famous for his westerns such as *She Wore a Yellow Ribbon* (1949)?
9. Which violent action director made the films *The Dirty Dozen, The Flight of the Phoenix* and *Hustle*?
10. Which American film maker made many epic films on Biblical themes including *Sign of the Cross, Samson and Delilah*, and *The Ten Commandments*?

Films : General

1. Which film company boasted that they had 'more stars than there are in the heavens'?
2. Which Walt Disney film was the first attempt to combine visual images with concert music?
3. What is the connection between the film *Chitty-Chitty-Bang-Bang* and the numbers 007?
4. Which film of 1960 did Arthur Miller write for his wife Marilyn Monroe who was a star of the film?
5. What did the films *Who's Afraid of Virginia Woolf?*, *The Snake Pit* and *One Flew Over The Cuckoo's Nest* have in common?
6. Badger the Bull-terrier, Tao the Siamese cat and Luath a Labrador retriever were travelling companions in which Disney film?
7. What was the name of the film for which Henry Fonda achieved an Oscar, which was the final film before his death?

8. What do the following films have in common – *Iron Man, Body and Soul, Run With the Wind* and *The Harder They Fall*?

9. Name the first three James Bond films.

10. In what year was the first *King Kong* film released?

11. In what kind of institution was the film *The Loneliness of the Long Distance Runner* set?

12. Which secret society was featured in the film *The Godfather*?

13. In which city did the action of the film *The French Connection* take place?

14. What was the first horror film, released in the spring of 1908?

15. Whose music was used as the theme tune for the popular film *The Sting*?

16. Which film of 1985 starring Edward Fox, Scott Glen and Barbara Carrera concerns an attempt to spring Rudolf Hess from Spandau Prison?

17. What do the 1950s films *Strangers On A Train, Dial M For Murder* and *To Catch A Thief* have in common?

18. What was the title of the last and most terrifying chapter in *The Omen* trilogy of films with Damien as a grown man of 33?

19. Where is Tinsel Town?

20. In 1958 the first in what became a prolific series of *Carry On* films was released. Name this film.

21. What was the title of Walt Disney's first full-length cartoon?

22. The life of Billy Mills, the Sioux Indian runner who won the 10,000 metres for America in the 1964 Olympics, was told in a film of 1984. What was the title of this film?

23. Where was the first British sound-film studio built in 1931?

24. In television and films what name is given to the small chunk of wood, hidden from the camera, on which short actors stand to bring them up to the correct height for their role?

25. What do the films *Jaws, Close Encounters of the Third Kind* and *ET: The Extra-Terrestrial* have in common?
26. What was the title of John Wayne's final film of 1976?
27. The actress Vivienne Leigh played the leading female role of Scarlett O'Hara in one of the finest films ever made. Name the film.
28. In which film of 1984 did Sean Connery return to the role of James Bond?

Films : Musicals

1. Which famous musical composer and conductor won Oscars for *Gigi, My Fair Lady, Irma La Douce* and *Porgy and Bess*?
2. In which film did the actress Liza Minelli play the part of Sally Bowles?
3. What was the title of the first successful sound movie picture made in 1927 and starring Al Jolson?
4. In *Singing in the Rain* what is the name of the film whose production is interrupted and plagued by the introduction of sound to the silent movies?
5. *Second Hand Rose, People, Sadie, Sadie* and *You are woman, I am man* are songs from which film?
6. Which famous musical group starred in the film *Rock around the Clock*?
7. Which film of 1934 gained an Oscar for the song *The Continental*?
8. Name the four films made by The Beatles.
9. What was the title of the 1956 film in which Elvis Presley made his film debut?
10. In 1940 Bob Hope and Bing Crosby starred in *Road to Singapore*. A total of seven films were made in this series, six of them by which American studio?

11. Can you name the actress who sang *Moon River* in the film *Breakfast at Tiffany's*?

12. In which film do you hear the happy chimney sweep (Dick Van Dyke) singing *Chim Chim Cheree* in order to brighten up some dispirited children?

13. Which actress stunned audiences as the provocative gangster's moll in *Singin' in the Rain* and starred with Fred Astaire in *Silk Stockings*?

14. *You've Got To Pick a Pocket Or Two* was a song from which popular British film of 1968?

15. With which film do you associate the song *Ding-Dong! The Witch Is Dead,* sung upon the accidental death of the Wicked Witch of the North?

16. Who starred in the film entitled *Hans Christian Andersen* and sang the songs *The Ugly Duckling* and *Thumbelina*?

17. The songs *See me, feel me, What about the boy* and *I'm free* were all from which popular film of 1975?

18. Lee Marvin's hit single in 1970 was the theme tune for which popular film?

19. Which actress starred in *Show Boat, The Barefoot Contessa* and *The Night of the Iguana*?

20. *The Bare Necessities* was nominated for an Oscar in 1967. From which film was this song taken?

21. Who was the debonair king of the British musical in the 1930s when Jessie Matthews was the queen?

22. *My Favourite Things* and *Maria* were popular songs from which film of the sixties?

Films : Names & Nicknames

1. What was Norma Jean Baker's other name?
2. Which famous film star was born William Henry Pratt in 1887?
3. Who was known throughout the world as the 'King of Comedy'?
4. Which early film star was widely known as the 'World's Sweetheart'?
5. Born in 1925, this actor made his debut in *Fighter Squadron*. He later came to be nicknamed 'The Baron of Beefcake'. Can you name him?
6. Groucho and Zeppo were two of the famous Marx Brothers comedy team – name the other two.
7. What was the nickname by which the American silent actor G M Anderson was better known?
8. Which actor was known as 'King of the Cowboys' from 1943, and also had the smartest horse in the movies?
9. Marion Morrison, originally a professional American footballer, changed his name to become a famous film star. By what name was he known?
10. Name Marilyn Monroe's husbands.

Food & Drink : Drinks

1. With what is the Belgian beer Kriek flavoured?
2. Tequila is a spirit originating from which country?
3. Angostura bitters are an ingredient in many cocktails. From where does angostura originate?
4. From what is vodka made?
5. From what is rum distilled?
6. What is the German label term indicating a high quality wine?
7. Sangria is a cold drink of red wine and fizzy lemonade decorated with fruit. From which country does it originate?
8. From what is the liqueur Calvados made and where in the world does it originate?
9. Which famous American drink was 'born' in Atlanta, Georgia, in 1886?
10. What is the name of the sparkling wine made in Piedmont, Italy? It is a white, highly scented, medium sweet variety.
11. Name the good-quality greenish-white wine from a town of the same name south-east of Paris.
12. Which fortified wine is named after the largest of a group of five Portuguese islands off the north west coast of Africa where it is made?
13. Which term describes a wine which has a large alcohol content?
14. Mead is a fermented drink, popular in Northern Europe from the very early times. From what is it made?
15. What is the name of the Scottish liqueur which is

made of whisky and heather honey?

16. On a bottle of cognac, what is meant by three stars?
17. What is the name of the popular Greek liqueur, flavoured with aniseed?
18. There are two main types of sherry. Can you name them?
19. What colour is Chartreuse, the brandy liqueur made near Grenoble?
20. What is the name of the Japanese native drink made from rice which is usually drunk warm?
21. Why is the drink Bourbon so called?
22. Isinglass is often used to clear wine and beer. From where is isinglass obtained?
23. What type of drink is Barack? It is very popular in Hungary.
24. How many years does vintage port take to reach its proper maturity?
25. Sekt and Perelada are what types of wine?
26. What is the name of the Irish whiskey which is illicitly made from barley?
27. What does the term 'brut' mean when referring to wine?
28. What is the Spanish word for a medium dry sherry?
29. Aperitifs can be broken down into three categories. What are they?
30. Which drink do you associate with Holy Island in Northumberland?
31. What is the name of the perfume given off by wine?
32. What is the name of the popular Italian wine from the region between Florence and Siena?
33. By what name do the English call the light red wines of Bordeaux?
34. What is the name of the Scandinavian alcoholic spirit made from potatoes?

Food & Drink : Name that Food

1. What name is given to the pudding which consists of ice cream, mounted on sponge cake and entirely covered with meringue?
2. Name the Italian, semi-soft, rich cheese with blue veins through it.
3. 'Love apple' is an old name for which fruit?
4. Which delicacy from Perigord in France is included in expensive varieties of pâté de fois gras?
5. Which cereal is obtained from the roots of the cassava plant?
6. What is the north-country name for crumpets?
7. Which fruit is known by the scientific name of *Malus pumila*?
8. The deficiency of a vitamin, found in fresh fruit and vegetables, was the principal cause of scurvy in the early days of the British Navy. What was the vitamin?
9. What name is given to a sugar syrup which is gently heated until it browns?
10. What type of soup is a Dubarry?
11. What is the name of the liquid butter made from cow or buffalo milk, which is used in Eastern countries?
12. What name is given to a round cake of pastry which is filled with a currant mixture?
13. What is the name of the fine blue cheese made from ewe's milk in south-west France?
14. What name do the Australians give to a pastry made with almonds, sugar and cream?
15. What name is given to small shaped pieces of toasted and fried bread garnished with caviar, smoked sal-

mon, anchovies, shrimps, etc?

16. What name is given to a side of unsliced bacon?
17. Name the most nutritious and least nutritious fruits in the world.
18. What name is given to very small cubes of fried bread served with soups?
19. Which cheese is known as the king of English cheeses?
20. What name is given to the fruit of the blackthorn?
21. What name is given to a two-coloured oblong cake, usually covered with almond paste?
22. What is the name of the hot, emulsified sauce containing egg yolks, butter and lemon juice?
23. What is the name of the fruit sauce which is a traditional accompaniment to the Christmas turkey?
24. Which edible nut of the American hickory tree is similar to a walnut?

Food & Drink : Traditional Dishes

1. What is the name of the Indian unleavened bread which is baked on a griddle and served with curry?
2. In which area of the world is Kharouf Mahshi a traditional dish?
3. What is the name of the traditional English dish which is made up of leftover food, usually potato, cabbage and other greens, which are fried?
4. What name is given to a kind of thin pancake which is eaten throughout Mexico?
5. Which country would you associate with the dish Couscous?

6. What is the name of the Turkish dish of vine leaves filled with rice, chopped meat and onions?
7. What is the name of the highly flavoured east Indian soup made with curry powder and hot seasonings?
8. What is the name of the Italian dish of large tubes of pasta filled with a savoury meat mixture?
9. Which vegetable is the traditional Burns Night accompaniment to haggis?
10. Blue Vinney is a famous English cheese. From which part of the country does it come?
11. Yellowish brown raw cane sugar is called demerara sugar after the region where it is produced – but where is Demerara?
12. What name is given to the group of Italian cheeses which are hard and old, and have a special strong taste? They are usually grated and used as flavourings.
13. Which cake is traditionally eaten on 5th November to commemorate Guy Fawkes?
14. What is the traditional Thanksgiving dessert served in the United States?
15. What is the name of the currant biscuit named after an 18th century Italian leader?
16. Osso Bucco is a traditional dish from Italy. What type of meat is usually used in the preparation of this dish?
17. What do Americans call endive?
18. What is the name of the cake, originally made for Mother's Day, but which became more identified with Easter over time?
19. The biscuit known as shortbread is a speciality from which country?
20. What do the Italians call their strong dark coffee served in small cups?

Food & Drink : What is it?

1. Give the culinary name for a bunch of herbs used in flavourings.
2. What name is given to a small fireproof dish used for cooking small portions of food?
3. Which cooking term is used to describe vegetables cut into very thin strips and cooked slowly in butter?
4. What does the phrase *al dente* mean?
5. What is bouillon?
6. What is a compote?
7. What cooking term is given to a garnish of spinach?
8. 'Plashing' is a term used to describe the collecting or gathering of what kind of nuts?
9. What is pumpernickel?
10. What are bigoli, farfalle, rigati and pansotti?
11. What are sometimes called Chinese Gooseberries?
12. Gnocchi is a food from Italy. What is it?
13. If you were served crudités as a starter before your main meal what would you be eating?
14. Which vegetable is also known as the spinach beet or seakale beet?
15. Kale is a variety of which winter vegetable?
16. What is gazpacho?
17. Petit Fours means literally 'little ovens'. What are they?
18. What is beeswing?
19. What is sauerkraut?
20. In Italy, if you were served pesce martello, what would you be about to eat?
21. Umbles can be made into a pie and gave rise to the expression 'to eat (h)umble pie'. What are umbles?
22. Agar-agar is often used in cooking. What is it?

Games & Pastimes

1. What do the opposite faces on a die total?
2. Which playing card is referred to as the Black Lady?
3. How many compartments are there on a roulette wheel?
4. When can a player of chess move two pieces at the same time?
5. For what are Tarot or Taroc cards used?
6. A game played with a small hour-glass-shaped object spun on a string fastened to two sticks was once known as 'the devil on two sticks'. By what name is it more familiarly known?
7. In Scrabble, how many additional points are gained if all seven letters are played in one turn?
8. How many men has each player in a game of backgammon?
9. In the game of Beetle specially prepared dice are needed with letters instead of spots. What are these letters?
10. What is the game, of Chinese origin, resembling dominoes and played with small tiles as pieces?
11. What is the national game of the people of the Basque country in France?
12. Court cards on British playing cards are costumed as of the time of which Monarch?
13. In bridge, what jargon word is used to describe the condition of holding no trumps?
14. Describe the game of skill colloquially known as 'ducks and drakes'.
15. Which popular card game is also known as Vingt-et-un, Blackjack and 21?

16. How many playing pieces are there in a set of dominoes?
17. African dominoes is another name for what?
18. Can you name the six murder weapons in the British game of *Cluedo*?
19. How many triple score squares are there on a Scrabble board?
20. In an ordinary deck of playing cards, the Jacks of Hearts and Spades are pictured in profile, whilst the Jacks of Diamonds and Clubs have full face portraits. How many Jacks' eyes are visible in the deck of cards?
21. What did a Budapest-based teacher of three dimensional design invent in the late '70s which took the western world by storm in the early '80s?
22. Playing cards are sometimes know as the Devil's Picture Books, but what are Devil's Bones?
23. How does a castle or rook move in a game of chess?
24. In canasta, how many playing cards are needed?
25. How many tricks are there in a grand slam in the game of bridge?
26. How many tiles are there in the game Mah-Jong?
27. Where would you find the Fool, the Juggler, the female Pope and the Hanged Man?
28. From which country did the card game bridge originate?
29. What is the name of the game which resembles billiards and is played with numbered cups instead of pockets?
30. Which playing card is referred to as 'the curse of Scotland'?
31. It is derived from a Turkish word meaning towel. What is the craft which comprises knotting threads and cords to create works of art?
32. How many squares are there on a chess board?

General Knowledge

1. The farandole is a traditional dance from which country?
2. What are the names of the four Inns of Court which call candidates to the Bar?
3. How many feet are in a fathom?
4. What famous worldwide organisation developed from a pamphlet called *Un Souvenir de Solferino* written by a Swiss – Jean Henri Dunant – in 1862?
5. Which item of furniture may be described as a cricket, drum, eagle, hutch or Sutherland?
6. How many points are there to the compass?
7. In the USA there are four time zones. Can you name them?
8. For what is the Queen Elizabeth Coronation Award given?
9. 'A factory in a garden village' was the idea of George and Richard Cadbury in 1879. What was this village named?
10. What is the name of the dog in the Punch and Judy show?
11. Which national organisation requires a belief in the Great Architect of the Universe?
12. What name is given to a marriage between a man or woman of royal or noble birth to a partner of inferior status with the provision that their children, though legitimate, shall have no claim to the rank or property?
13. What name is given to the hard reddish brick-like earthenware which is porous and unglazed?
14. What was the title of the first women's magazine,

published in 1693?

15. For what is the 'James A Reid' Championship Shield awarded?

16. Which mineral substance, found near Whitby and the Yorkshire coast, is popularly used in jewellery?

17. If a gold item bore the number 375, what carat rating would the article be?

18. Name the seven colours of the rainbow.

19. What name is given to a giant revolving vertical wheel which supports passenger cars on its rim, as seen in funfairs? It is named after the American engineer who invented it.

20. Which statutory body was created by the Development of Tourism Act of 1969?

21. How many characters are there in the Greek alphabet?

22. The sea around the coast of Great Britain is divided into different areas for weather forecasting purposes. What is the area known as which surrounds the Orkney and Shetland islands?

23. The Pulitzer Prize annual awards were first given in 1917 for achievements in which American fields?

24. What is the name of the remarkably light and strong wood which is very useful for making model aircraft and boats?

25. What name is given to the tent in which a circus takes place?

26. James Bond has the Secret Service designation 007. What is the meaning of 007?

27. Add together the following Roman numbers: CM, XC, LX.

28. In conversation, what would be the correct form of address to a duke who is not a member of the Royal Family?

29. With reference to furniture, what is the name of the transparent gum made of shellac dissolved in methylated spirit?

30. When the European Economic Community (EEC) was formed by the Treaty of Rome in 1957, it con-

sisted of six countries. Can you name four of them?

31. Big Ben is the famous Bell which stands beside the Houses of Parliament in London. How many faces has the clock on Big Ben's tower?

32. In Britain, how often is the National Census held?

33. In bullfighting, what name is given to the men who ride on horses and carry large lances?

34. If your hobby was scrimshaw, what would you be making?

35. Plexiglas is a trademark in the USA. What is its British equivalent?

36. What was the name of the blue and white designed pottery attributed to the Staffordshire potter Thomas Minton around 1780?

37. Release is a helping organisation. With what type of problem is it concerned?

38. The Watusi or Batutsi tribe comes from Burundi in Central Africa. What is this tribe remarkable for?

39. Which is the oldest of the European universities?

40. According to the *Boy Scout Handbook,* what are the six regulation knots?

41. How many chains are there in a mile?

42. What is a period of one thousand years called?

43. Which organisation was set up in Britain to help one-parent families?

44. When was the radio-only licence fee abolished?

45. Which letter of the alphabet is used to denote an unknown quantity?

46. Where in Great Britain do witnesses in courts swear to tell the truth 'as I shall to God at the great day of judgment'?

47. What is the Roman numeral for one thousand?

48. What is the name of the oldest educational institution in the USA, founded in 1636?

49. What is the name of the Brazilian dance which resembles the samba?

50. What is the name of the bell which hangs in the underwriters' room in Lloyd's of London?

51. Whose original site was in Whitehall, near Charing Cross, London, and in 1890 moved to near Westminster Bridge and then to Broadway, Westminster, in 1967?

52. A horse is measured in hands. How many centimetres is a hand?

53. What was the name of the first residential university college founded in 1899 for working people?

54. What is meant by the law of ancient lights?

55. The waltz is a popular ballroom dance. How many beats in the bar has the waltz?

56. General Sherman stands in the Sequoia National Park in California. What is it?

57. What is the name of the highest award in the Boys' Brigade which is given for regular attendance and skill in various activities?

58. How many degrees are there in a circle?

59. How long is the Great Wall of China?

60. Who was the respectable Victorian gentleman who spent virtually all his life becoming the King of Saucy Postcards?

61. How many degrees are there, in total, in the angles of a triangle?

62. With which section of the community is the organisation CRUSE concerned?

63. English pieces of silver usually have no fewer than four marks (hallmarks). What are these marks?

64. In needlework, which stitch may be described as petit point?

65. Which Latin American dance is performed by persons in a single file following a leader?

66. Who was the sweetheart of Harlequin who, like him, was supposed to be invisible to mortal eyes?

67. What is the name of the authoritative and complete reference book where the method of time-keeping in every part of the world can be found?

68. With what is canon law concerned?

69. Which hardwood used in cabinet-making and inlaying

is also used for piano keys and knife-handles?
70. What would be the nationality of a stamp with the word 'Suomi' printed on it?
71. Where would you find the Dewey Decimal system in use?

Geographical Terms

1. By what name is the parallel of latitude 23½°N of the equator commonly known?
2. A rhea is a flightless bird but what does the geographical term 'ria' mean?
3. What name is given to a region of high air pressure, the highest pressure occurring at the centre?
4. What, in geographical terms, is the Prime Meridian?
5. What is the name of the hot southerly wind that blows from the Sahara across Southern Italy?
6. What is the study of earthquakes called?
7. If the latitude of the equator is 0°, what is the latitude of the North Pole?
8. What name is given to the scientific observation and study of the phenomena of weather?
9. What is a metamorphic rock?
10. What name is given to hot springs that throw out huge streams of boiling water? (They can be seen in the Yellowstone region of America and in New Zealand.)
11. What name is given to the imaginary line on the earth's surface which lies 66°33' South of the Equator?
12. What is a drumlin?
13. What do the following have in common: Washington,

Peterlee, Livingstone, Cwmbran, Crawley and Basildon?

14. What term is used to describe the height of a place above mean sea level?

15. According to the Beaufort Scale, what number is assigned to a hurricane?

16. Where would you find the San Andreas Fault?

17. What name is given to the vast treeless plains in North America and northern Russia where long severe winters and permanently frozen subsoils have resulted in specially adapted plant communities?

18. What name is given to a sharp mountain ridge with steep sides formed by erosion?

19. What is the Mistral?

20. What is the name given to the molten substance emitted from a volcano?

21. What name is given to a whirling tornado-like cloud occurring at sea?

22. What term is used to describe a series of waterfalls? It is also sometimes used to describe rapids.

Geography : Islands

1. An island off the west coast of Canada is separated from the mainland by the Juan de Fuca Strait. Its capital is Victoria. What is the island?

2. Montserrat is an island in which West Indian group?

3. Name the only town on the Scottish Island of Mull.

4. Ibiza, Formentera, Majorca, Minorca and Cabrera collectively form which group of islands?

5. Which island off Guernsey is noted for the absence of cars from its shores?

6. Which group of islands in Portuguese possession lies some 800 miles west of Portugal?

7. In which ocean are the Maldive Islands?

8. Three of the world's largest islands are situated in the Indian Ocean. What are they?

9. What is the name of the island in New York Harbour which was used as an immigrant station until 1954?

10. Name the largest island in the world.

11. The colony of Tanganyika in the East of Africa joined with which island to create the Republic of Tanzania in 1963?

12. On which island would you find Beaumaris Castle, the building of which was begun in 1295?

13. What is the largest and southernmost of the Greek Islands?

14. On which Mediterranean island is the town of Ajaccio?

15. On which island country would you find a mountain called Adam's Peak and a chain of islands called Adam's Bridge?

16. What are the Tonga Islands otherwise known as?

17. To which country does the island of Elba belong?

18. By what name do we more commonly refer to the Islas Malvinas?

19. In what island group would you find Herm, Sark and Alderney?

20. Which island is the most easterly of the West Indies and whose chief industry is tourism?

21. Its name translates into English as The Land of Fire. Name this island off the southern coast of Argentina.

22. By what other name do we know the Somers Islands?

23. Mount Albert, Mount Eden and One Tree Hill were once volcanoes on which island?

24. Name the largest of the Society Islands which were visited by Captain Cook (1769) and by Captain Bligh of *HMS Bounty* (1788).

25. The island of Malta forms only part of the independent state of Malta. What is the name of the other

smaller island off its northern coast?

26. On which island would you find the Old Man of Hoy rock stack?

27. Name 3 of the populated islands forming the Isles of Scilly.

28. Which island was the headquarters of the Knights of St John from 1530, became French in 1798 and British in 1814?

29. What is the alternative name for Holy Island, the island off the north coast of Northumberland?

30. On which island are the former British colonies of Sarawak and Brunei?

31. Inishmore is the largest of which group of islands?

32. Which Scottish island is separated from the mainland by the Sound of Sleat?

33. Fuerteventura, Gomera and La Palma form part of which island group?

34. What and where are the Aleutians?

35. What is the name of the group of islands in the North Atlantic which belong to Denmark, the capital of which is Thorshavn?

36. Yell, Fetlar, Papa Stour and Foula are among which group of islands?

37. To which European country do the island groups of the Cyclades and the Dodecanese belong?

38. Puffin Island gets its name from the seabirds who breed there. Where is Puffin Island?

39. Of which island republic is Antananarivo the capital?

40. Which of the following islands is the largest: Ireland, Cuba, Sumatra, Iceland, Tasmania or Newfoundland?

41. On what island is Fingal's Cave?

42. Where in the world would you find Amsterdam Island, Kerguelen, Crozet Island and McDonald Island?

43. What is the largest of the West Indian islands?

44. What is the name of the lighthouse which lies west of the Scilly Isles and is in one of the most exposed

82

positions in the world?

45. This group of islands is located in the Caribbean Sea, south of Cuba. The principal island, which gives its name to the group, is 178 miles west of Jamaica. What is the name of these islands?

46. Which island, located in the south-eastern Pacific Ocean, is noted for its many huge stone-sculptured images?

47. What are the Florida Keys?

48. Which is the most southerly of the Channel Islands?

Geography :
Mountains & Volcanoes

1. Mount Aconcagua in South America is nearly 23,000 feet high. In which country is it situated?

2. What is the highest mountain in the North American continent?

3. In which country would you find the Drakensberg Mountains?

4. Name the volcano on the European mainland whose eruption in AD 79 destroyed the cities of Pompeii and Herculaneum.

5. What is the name of the range of hills that runs along the border between Scotland and England?

6. The Himalayan Mountain Range has the highest peaks in the world but at 2,400 miles is only the third longest range. What is the world's longest range?

7. What is the name of the mountain pass between Afghanistan and North West Pakistan?

8. Mount Kosciusko is the highest peak of a range of

mountains in which country?

9. What name is given to the valley in Alaska, USA, where the eruption of Mt Katmai, in 1912, was one of the largest volcanic explosions ever known?
10. What is the highest peak in the United Kingdom south of the Scottish border?
11. In which country would you find the Laurentian Mountains?
12. Dunkery Beacon is the highest peak in which British National Park?
13. What is the name of the highest active volcano in Europe? It is situated on an island in the Mediterranean Sea.
14. What famous mountain, the highest in Japan, is considered to be sacred by some Japanese?
15. Where in Britain would you find the Sperrin Mountains?
16. What is the highest mountain in the continent of Africa?
17. In which country is the volcanic mountain called Popacatapetl?
18. Which is the only one of the ten highest mountains in the world which is not in the Himalayas?
19. Monte Marmolada is the highest peak of which mountain range?
20. White, Green, Catskill, Allegheny, Blue Ridge and Black are all parts of which mountain range?
21. The greatest mountain system is the Himalaya range with 104 peaks. What is the second greatest range, with 54 peaks?
22. Where in the world is the range of mountains known as the Southern Alps?
23. What is the highest mountain in the world?
24. The Pindus mountains are the principal mountain range of which country?
25. Which range of mountains separates France from Spain?
26. Mount Zeil is the highest peak of the MacDonnell

Ranges. Where are they located?

27. Where in the world would you find Macgillicuddy's Reeks?

28. Devil's Peak and Lion's Heart are part of which mountain?

29. Name the highest mountain in the Alps.

30. What is the name of the mountain range which runs down the backbone of Italy?

31. Mauna Loa, Mount Spurr, Lassen Peak, Kilauea and Mount St Helens are all mountains in the USA. What is the most significant feature of all these mountains?

32. Name the oldest mountains in the United States which rise to 1600 metres in New York State.

Geography :
Regions, Countries & States

1. By what name is Portuguese West Africa now known?

2. In order of size, Alaska is the biggest State of the USA and Texas is the second. What is the third biggest state in the USA?

3. By what name is Van Diemen's land better known?

4. Badwater is the western hemisphere's lowest point. Where is it found?

5. By what name was the African State of Namibia formerly known?

6. Which country has taken its name from a line of latitude?

7. Washington DC and Canberra are planned capital cities. What capital city was planned to replace Rio de Janeiro?

8. Transylvania is, according to fiction writers, the homeland of the Vampires, but where in reality is Transylvania?

9. Can you name the smallest and largest Canadian provinces?

10. What name was given to the free-slave Republic established in West Africa in 1847?

11. What name is given to the coastal region province of southern Portugal?

12. Adelie Land is a French territory in the coastal region of which continent?

13. Which is the smallest independent state in the world?

14. What country is known as the 'land of cakes'?

15. Which country has common borders with Argentina, Bolivia and Brazil?

16. Which of the American states is known as the Volunteer State?

17. It was formerly known as Nyasaland. By what name is it now known?

18. What is the most northerly point of Ireland?

19. Where would you find the Bronx?

20. Which country has the reputation of being the Breadbasket of the World?

21. Alba is the Celtic name for which country?

22. The Republic of Zaire in Central Africa was formerly known as the Republic of the Congo, following independence in 1960. Which European country colonized the Congo?

23. It used to be called Formosa – what is it now called?

24. Which English county is often referred to as the gateway of England?

25. What South American country was named after an Italian city because of its abundance of surface water?

26. It was formerly known as East Pakistan. By what name is it now known?

27. By what name are Peebleshire, Selkirkshire, Roxburghshire and Berwickshire collectively known?

28. Hammerfest is the most northerly town in the world.

In which country is it?
29. Limoges is famous for its porcelain and ceramics. In which country is it situated?
30. Which state of America is known as the Lone Star State because of the single star on its flag which dates back to 1836–45 when it was independent from the Union?
31. By what name do we now know British Honduras?
32. What name is given to the headland on the coast of Essex, south of Harwich?
33. Mecca, the holiest city of the Mohammedan world, is in which country?
34. It used to be known as Siam, but what is it now known as?
35. What name is given to the great fertile plain of South America which is about twice the size of the British Isles?
36. Name the states which comprise the Benelux countries.
37. In which state of the United States is the Grand Canyon?
38. In which country is the province of Andalusia?
39. Which Welsh county, created in 1974, was formerly known as Monmouthshire?
40. What is the name of the port of south west Uruguay known as an important meat packing and canning centre?
41. What is the name of the small independent state located between France and Spain in the High Pyrenees?
42. The N'Gorongoro Crater is a magnificent game reserve in which famous Tanzanian National Park?
43. Which town in Spain has long been noted for the manufacture of high quality steel swords?
44. Which country is known as the Emerald Isle?
45. What is the name given to the valley between Loch Achray and Loch Katrine in Scotland?
46. Where is Labrador – the region which has given its name to the breed of dog called Labrador Retrievers?

Geography : Towns & Cities

1. Of which country is Damascus the capital?
2. Which capital city stands on the Potomac river?
3. Which town of Strathclyde in central Scotland was created as a 'new town' in 1955?
4. What is the capital city of Indonesia?
5. Karachi is the chief seaport of which country?
6. What is the capital of West Virginia in the USA?
7. Suez lies at one end of the Suez Canal – what is the city at the other end?
8. What is the most northerly town of the British Isles?
9. What is the capital city of Sudan?
10. Can you give the two former names of the modern Turkish city of Istanbul?
11. Can you name the capital of Florida?
12. Which industrial city has the largest inland port in Europe?
13. Which city is known as The Big Apple?
14. What is the capital city of Afghanistan?
15. Which city was founded in 1793 by Lieutenant-Governor John Graves Simcoe?
16. Which port of Sicily shares its name with a city in New York State?
17. The city of Phoenix is the capital of which state of the USA?
18. Name the mining town in Gwent, Wales, which Aneurin Bevin represented in Parliament from 1926–60.
19. What is the main town of the principality of Monaco?
20. Concord is the capital of which American state?

21. What is the capital city and chief industrial centre of Northern Ireland?
22. What is the capital of Chile?
23. Istanbul is a city built upon seven famous hills. Which other capital city can claim a similar distinction?
24. What is the capital city of Uruguay?
25. What is the name of the Cumbrian town on the River Eden which has an annual horse fair?
26. In which city is Madison Square Garden?
27. Antwerp is the chief port in which country?
28. What is the capital of Iceland?
29. Which European capital city stands on the River Liffey?
30. Which town of the Tayside region of Scotland is famous for its smoked haddock and was the scene of Robert I's Declaration of Independence (1320)?
31. Which town in south-east Ontario, Canada, shares its name with a county in south-west England?
32. Of the many famous beaches in the world Copacabana is one of the most famous. By which city is it situated?
33. The Plains of Abraham overlook which city?
34. In which city would you find the Jacques Cartier Bridge?
35. Name the capital of Sicily.
36. The Road to Mandalay featured in a World War II song. Of which country was Mandalay once the capital?
37. What is the capital of Colorado?
38. What is the capital of the American state of Massachusetts?
39. In which city would you find the Spanish Steps?
40. Of which country is Asuncion the capital city?
41. Name the oldest city in Germany which lies on the left bank of the Rhine.
42. Which 'fort' is a resort town of south-east Florida?
43. What is the capital of New York State?
44. Which city in Ontario is known as Steel City of Canada?

45. What is the capital of Cuba?
46. What is the capital of the Bahamas?
47. What is the capital city of the Northern Territory of Australia?
48. What is the name of the fishing port in Scotland's Grampian region which was Ramsay MacDonald's birthplace and also where he was buried?
49. What is the capital of Canada?
50. Name the city and chief seaport of Egypt at the mouth of the River Nile.
51. Of which European city is Piraeus the port?
52. What is the capital of Denmark?
53. Which town is known as the capital of the Cotswolds?
54. What is the capital of the Philippines?
55. Which city stands on the River Spree and the River Havel?
56. Name the capital city of Tanzania.
57. What is the capital of Morocco?
58. Which city in New Zealand is known both as the City of the Plains and the Garden City?
59. Name the capital of the Highlands of Scotland.
60. The Bowery was a street in which city, which was formerly known for its criminal population and distinctive dialect?

Geography :
Water & Waterways

1. Where is the Gulf of Carpentaria?
2. In which country does the River Danube rise?
3. What is the name of the important canal in Egypt?

4. What is the name of the largest lake in Italy which is a popular tourist resort?

5. Which river forms the major part of the international boundary between the United States of America and Mexico?

6. Name the American port which is located at the mouth of the Mississippi River?

7. Name the sea channel which separates the island of Tierra del Fuego from the South American sub-continent?

8. Name the canal which stretches from Fort William on the west coast to Inverness on the east coast.

9. On the banks of which river was the city of Rome built?

10. Where would you find the Gatun Lake, the Gaillard Cut and the Miraflores Locks?

11. What is the name of the world's largest freshwater lake?

12. Which British river is particularly noted for its tidal bore?

13. Which sea joins the North Channel with the St George's Channel?

14. By what name is the largest inland salt water lake in the world known?

15. What is the name of the Strait which separates North Island from South Island in New Zealand?

16. In Norway the long, deep inlets of the sea flanked by mountainous cliffs are called fjords. By what name are similar land formations known in New Zealand?

17. What is the name of the channel between Hampshire and the Isle of Wight?

18. Name the four longest rivers in the world.

19. Which river flows into the Dead Sea?

20. The Windrush, Evenlode, Colne, Lea, Kennet, Loddon and Mole are all tributaries of which river?

21. What do the Dead Sea, the Caspian Sea and the Salton Sink in California have in common – other than water?

22. Between which two of Canada's Great Lakes do the Niagara Falls lie?

23. What is the nickname of the famous geyser or waterspout in Yellowstone National Park in the Rockies in America?

24. Measured by its shoreline, which is the largest bay in the world?

25. What name is given to a sea containing many islands, such as the Aegean Sea between Greece and Turkey? (The term is also used to mean a group of islands.)

26. Which two English cities did the Grand Union Canal link?

27. Name the only one of the Great Lakes to be wholly in the USA.

28. What name is given to a dry watercourse in a desert?

29. Name the stretch of water which separates the Inner Hebrides from the Outer Hebrides.

30. Which is the longest river in the world?

31. Into which ocean does the Zambesi River flow?

32. The Marne, Oise and Aube are tributaries of which great river?

33. Which is the largest sea in the world?

34. What name is given to the Strait which divides the city of Constantinople and links the Black Sea with the Sea of Marmara?

35. Antwerp is one of the world's most important ports, though it lies 55 miles from the sea. On which river is it?

36. What is the name of the inlet of the Irish Sea between south-west Scotland and north-west England?

37. The Sutherland Falls are among the highest in the world. Where are they situated?

38. Name the longest river in France.

39. Iraq was once part of Mesopotamia which, translated, means 'between two rivers' – which two rivers?

40. Into which sea does the River Volga discharge?

41. What is the name of the narrow strait between Europe and Asiatic Turkey?

42. What famous tourist attraction is wearing away at the rate of five feet per annum?
43. What name is given to the sea-route from the Atlantic round the north of Canada to the Pacific?
44. Can you name the deepest lake in Europe?
45. In which ocean are the Kara Sea, the Beaufort Sea and the Lincoln Sea situated?
46. Which stretch of water separates Sicily from Italy?
47. What is the name of the longest river in Italy?
48. Lake Balaton is the largest in central Europe. In which country is it?
49. What is the name of the channel which links the Kattegat with the North Sea?
50. The tributaries of which river include the Inn, Sava, Tisza and Prut?
51. What name is given to the part of the Thames immediately below London Bridge?
52. Where would you find the highest waterfall in the world?
53. Which sea is sometimes referred to as the Mediterranean of the North?
54. On which river do the cities of Quebec and Montreal stand?
55. What is the name of the largest lake in South America, beside which is the most famous modern shrine of South America, *The Virgin of Light*?
56. What is the longest river in the British Isles?
57. What is the Australian name for a kind of long narrow lake?
58. Name the major river in Norway.
59. What is the name of the large sand bank in the North Sea, off Northumberland?
60. Which 200 mile stretch of waterways in East Anglia has become one of the most popular holiday haunts in Britain?

Great Britain

1. Which English market town in Leicestershire is famous as a hunting and horsebreeding centre and for its Stilton cheeses and pork pies?
2. When the light shines above the belfry on Big Ben what does this signify?
3. Where, in the north-east of England, was the first life-boat station established?
4. Where would you find Arthur's Seat?
5. Which British city was known as cottonopolis?
6. What is the most southerly point of England?
7. What would you find 21 kilometres south of Plymouth?
8. Which new town in Shropshire is named after a famous engineer who worked in the area?
9. What is another name for the county of Shropshire?
10. What name is given to the seat occupied by the Lord Chancellor of the House of Lords?
11. Which famous zoo would you find near Dunstable in Bedfordshire?
12. In which city are the remains of the *Mary Rose* preserved?
13. Where in Britain would you find an imitation of the Eiffel Tower?
14. Which Lakeland village is the setting, every August, of the famous Lakeland Sports?
15. In Cambridge, behind the ancient university colleges are a network of canals. What are they called?
16. What is the name of the celebrated village, just over the border from England, where runaway couples

were married from 1754–1856?

17. Which English city was the birthplace of Guy Fawkes and the place of execution of Dick Turpin?

18. What is the name of the Royal Park which was enclosed by Charles I as part of a hunting estate and still has large herds of red and fallow deer?

19. The biggest funfair in England is in Staffordshire. Can you name it?

20. The Pennine Way is a magnificent hill walk from Edale in Derbyshire, along the Pennines over the Cheviots to the Scottish border. How many miles is it?

21. The pupils of which English Public School are referred to as New Coll. Men?

22. The Royal Oak is a popular name for public houses in Britain. They are named after which king?

23. Name the only city in England whose ancient walls are complete.

24. What do Ermine Street, Watling Street and Fosse Way have in common?

25. St Johnstown at one time held claim to be the capital of Scotland. By what name is it now known?

26. The Royal Mint was housed in a building on Tower Hill until the opening of the New Royal Mint in 1968. Where is the New Royal Mint?

27. Grace Darling and her father rescued nine survivors from the wrecked *SS Forfarshire* one stormy night in 1838. Various relics associated with the heroine, including the rowing boat, can be seen in the Grace Darling Museum. Where is this?

28. Where in England would you find Roedean Girls' School?

29. The Speaker's Chair is found in the Houses of Parliament. From which country did this chair originate?

30. Which market town in Cambridgeshire has the same name as a month of the year?

31. The Staffordshire area in and around Stoke-on-Trent

is famous for the manufacture of earthenware. By what name is the area more commonly known?

32. What is the name of the Atomic Energy Research Establishment in Berkshire, close to the Hampshire border?

33. In which National Park would you find the Prescelly Hills?

34. Name the main port of the Isle of Wight which is a famous yachting centre.

35. In which elegant English town would you find the Gustav Holst Museum (the birthplace of the composer)?

36. What is the name of the ancient Royal Palace in Edinburgh, still used as a royal residence, which dates from the fifteenth century?

37. Where would you find the Fitzwilliam Museum?

38. In which English County were the following famous people born: St Boniface, Francis Drake, Joshua Reynolds, Charles Kingsley and Agatha Christie?

39. Where is the head office of the Premium Savings Bonds?

40. On which islands is the ceremony of Uphellya celebrated after Christmas?

41. Which national institution did Sir William Hillary found in 1824?

42. Where in Britain would you be if you arrived at Temple Meads Railway Station?

43. Which English city is called the City of a Thousand Trades?

44. Only one canal runs through any of the British National Parks. In which of the National Parks would you find it?

45. How long is Hadrian's Wall? From which two places does it stretch?

46. Where was Rudolf Hess held in 1941 following his abortive attempt to make an 'honourable' peace after parachuting into Britain?

47. Name the library at Oxford University which is

famous for its collection of rare books and manuscripts.

48. 'Bobbing Hats' are the traditional headgear of which porters?
49. Which urban district of Essex was designated a new town in 1955, incorporating Essex's four boroughs?
50. What is the main language on the island of Anglesey?
51. Name the prison on the Isle of Wight built in 1830 which was originally for boys.
52. Which organisation maintains the lighthouses around the coasts of England and Wales?
53. From which tower of the New Palace of Westminster does the Union Jack fly by day?

History : Ancient – Mediaeval

1. Who was the Carthaginian general who overran southern Spain, Gaul, crossed the Alps and defeated the Romans at the Battle of Cannae?
2. What was the name of William the Conqueror's wife?
3. What name was given to the Roman Road connecting London to York via Lincoln?
4. Emperor Claudius was responsible for the subjugation of Britain. Who led the Britons and was defeated by Claudius at the Battle of the Medway in AD 43, was captured and later freed in Rome?
5. What was the name of the fortress in Paris, built in the fourteenth century and used as a state prison, especially for political prisoners?
6. Which is the oldest University in the United Kingdom?
7. The Romans, who invaded what is now called

Scotland in AD 80, called the people Picts. What did they call the country?

8. He was King of the Huns from Asia who defeated the Roman Emperor Theodosius and entered Gaul – but was defeated in AD 451 near Chalons-sur-Marne. Who was he?

9. Henry I is said to have died from a surfeit of his favourite fish. What was it?

10. Over which Empire did Montezuma rule before he was dethroned by Cortez?

11. What was Offa's Dyke?

12. Which king of England (1189–99) was the leader of the third crusade with Philip II of France?

13. Who was the Roman gladiator who headed the third revolt of slaves against Rome in 73–71 BC? He was eventually killed.

14. In mediaeval times there were three different kinds of guild. Craftsmen and religious were two – what was the third?

15. Which Roman Emperor issued the Edict of Milan and ended the persecution of Christians? He probably, in later life, became a Christian himself.

16. How did William the Conqueror find out how much his territories were worth after he conquered Britain in 1066?

17. Early English kings were often given nicknames. What nickname was given to King Ethelred II who died in 1016?

18. Peter the Hermit lived between 1050 and 1115. For what is he particularly known historically?

19. Which great emperor and leader, known for his bravery and wisdom, had a horse called Bucephalus?

20. Complete the sequence of Roman Emperors: Augustus, Tiberius, Caligula, Claudius, who?

21. Who, according to legend, was inspired to try again by watching the activities of a spider spinning a web?

22. To whom is attributed the construction of the Hanging Gardens of Babylon?

23. What was founded in 1440 by Henry VI to prepare scholars for King's College, Cambridge?

24. What London building was begun in 1245 by Henry III, replacing an earlier one built by Edward the Confessor?

25. By what name do we now know the former Roman strongholds Camulodunum and Verulamium?

26. Although the Inca civilization created a vast empire in Peru, they lacked basic skills and knowledge without which European civilization could not have advanced. Two of these were writing and the use of iron. What notable invention was also unknown to the Incas?

27. Which English King invented a candle clock?

28. Which people did Julius Caesar refer to as 'the bravest of the peoples of Gaul' as it took him over seven years to conquer them?

29. Boadicea or Boudicca was the queen of which British tribe?

30. Blondell traditionally followed King Richard I on the third crusade and discovered his master imprisoned in a German castle. What tradition or trade did Blondell practise?

31. Three English kings were killed by arrows – Richard, Coeur de Lion, in Chaluz in France, William Rufus in the New Forest – who was the third and where?

32. In 800 AD he was crowned by Pope Leo the Third in Rome as the First Holy Roman Emperor. Who was he?

33. The town of Herculaneum disappeared in 79 AD. Why?

34. Who was responsible for the construction of the Tower of London?

35. Who was the King of Munster in Ireland who defeated the Danes in 1002 AD and became the King of all Ireland?

36. The Punic Wars were fought in ancient times between Rome and which great rival Mediterranean city?

37. How long did the One Hundred Years War last?

38. What sea was referred to as Mare Nostrum by the Romans?
39. What, in English history, was the Danegeld?
40. In which battle did an invading army of 10,000 English, under Edward III, defeat 20,000 French men-at-arms in 1346?
41. Who was the son of Sweyn, King of Norway and Denmark, who drove King Ethelred the Unready from the throne of England?
42. What was sealed by King John at Runnymede on 15th June 1215?
43. What was the name of the Chinese dynasty (1368–1644) founded by Chu Yuan-chang which was noted for its literary excellence and fine porcelain?
44. Rome was the capital of the Roman Empire. Of what ancient empire was Persepolis the ceremonial centre?
45. In mediaeval times, what was a mangonel used for?
46. Which English King was defeated by Robert the Bruce at Bannockburn?
47. Which was the first of the Cambridge colleges to be founded, in 1284?

History : 16th–18th Centuries

1. What was the name of Henry VIII's chief minister who was dismissed after failing to persuade the Pope to grant him a divorce from Catharine of Aragon?
2. James Hepburn, the fourth Earl of Bothwell, died in 1578. Whom did he marry in 1567?
3. What name was given to those people who supported the House of Stuart's claim to the succession of the British throne?

4. Which British regiment of guards was first recruited by General Monk on the Tweed in 1659?

5. During which king's reign were the infamous Bloody Assizes held in England?

6. In 1776 the Liberty Bell was rung to signal what important event?

7. What did the 1697 Act of Habeas Corpus abolish?

8. The Treaty of Aix-la-Chapelle in 1748 ended which war?

9. By what title was Oliver Cromwell known?

10. The Fire of London of 1666 extended from east to west of the city. How many days did the fire last?

11. Prince Charles Edward Stuart was known as the Young Chevalier or the Young Pretender – but who in history was known as the Old Pretender?

12. Who was the first person to rule over the United Kingdom of Great Britain, after the 1707 Act of Union?

13. What name was given to the carts which carried the condemned prisoners to the guillotine during the French Revolution?

14. The Jacobites were defeated in which battle of 1746?

15. Who was President of the United States during the American Civil War?

16. She was an actress and favourite of Charles II. What was her name?

17. In 1793 Louis XVI and his wife were executed. Revolutionary France declared war on three countries. Can you name them?

18. What used to take place at Tyburn in Middlesex until 1783?

19. Corsairs were infamous during the 16th and 17th centuries. What kind of people were they?

20. On which date did America declare its independence from Britain?

21. What name was given to the meeting place of Henry VIII and François I of France, near Calais, in 1520, which was noted for the magnificence of the display made by the two kings?

22. The Royal Arms of Great Britain, dating from 1603, are supported by two figures. A lion represents England. What figure represents Scotland?

23. Which English explorer of the 17th century introduced tobacco and potatoes to England?

24. Name Henry VIII's three children who succeeded to the throne.

25. The proletariat of the French Revolution were given a name, meaning 'without breeches', because they wore trousers instead of the aristrocratic knee-breeches. What was this name?

26. What was the name of Sir Walter Raleigh's ship in the battle with the Armada?

27. What did Peter Minuit buy in 1626 from an Indian tribe for some trinkets valued at $24?

28. Which canal marked the beginning of canal building in industrial Britain in 1761?

29. Who was executed on 29th October 1618 after having spent the last 13 years of his life confined to the Tower of London?

30. What was the original name of Sir Francis Drake's ship the *Golden Hind*?

31. What was the name given to those who fought in support of Charles I during the English Civil War?

32. By what name is the Third Silesian War of 1756–63 more commonly known?

33. An epidemic of bubonic plague ravaged London in 1665, what name was this given?

34. Hawaii was the 50th and last state to join the United States of America. Name one of the first five states to form the Union in the years 1787–88?

35. Where in England was Mary Queen of Scots beheaded?

36. The British soldier, Robert Clive, won a series of victories, notably at Arcot (1751), Calcutta and Plassey (1757). How did he die?

37. Which inventor of the spinning frame is sometimes called the father of the industrial age?

38. Which island did the mutineers from *The Bounty* occupy and colonise in 1790?
39. Who was the Spanish king responsible for the Armada?
40. Which former marsh of Somerset was the scene of James II's victory over the Duke of Monmouth (1685)?
41. In which century was the Taj Mahal built?
42. The Rye House Plot was a conspiracy to assassinate which King in 1683?
43. What did Perkin Warbeck and Lambert Simnel have in common during the reign of Henry VII?
44. The Duke of Cumberland was given a nickname by the Highlanders following his treatment of the clans in 1746. What was this nickname?
45. Where did the Great Trek take place and who were the trekkers?

History : 19th–20th Century

1. In which battle was Nelson killed?
2. What was the name of the Argentine cruiser sunk after a British attack during the Falklands War in May 1982?
3. What was the great discovery made in 1922 by Howard Carter and Lord Caernarvon?
4. What was the name of the socialistic movement in England 1837–55 which attempted to better the conditions of the working classes?
5. Which country do you associate with the Easter Rising and in what year did it occur?
6. On 6th May 1937 a German airship was involved in a

disaster which claimed the lives of 33 people. What was its name?

7. In 1945, 24 Nazi leaders were put on trial for war crimes. Name these trials.

8. Which British Prime Minister was assassinated in 1812?

9. Who popularised the Christmas tree in England in the nineteenth century?

10. When did the Spanish Civil War take place?

11. Who became the first President of Malawi in 1971?

12. In a competition in 1829, what were Novelty, Rocket, Perseverance and Sans Pareil? Who won?

13. An Irish Society, founded in 1843, was given a peculiar name because its members dressed as women when carrying out acts of insurgence. What was the name of this Society?

14. Who were the two rival groups in the Battle of Blood River in 1838?

15. Whose assassination is said to have led to the out-break of the First World War and where did it happen?

16. What name was given to the six farm labourers from a Dorset village who formed a union to improve their conditions and were sentenced to transportation to Australia in 1834?

17. Who were known as the Fifth Column?

18. Which European country ruled the Philippine Islands as a colony before ceding them to the United States in 1898?

19. What was the remarkable venue for the meeting of Napoleon and the Czar of Russia in Tilsit in July 1807?

20. Which colony, and later major city of the world, did Sir Stamford Raffles found in 1819?

21. In the colonial scramble for Africa in the 1880s only two nations or states remained under native rule. Name one of them.

22. Which organisation was set up by the Bretton Wood Agreement of 1944 to promote international co-oper-

ation and remove foreign exchange restrictions?

23. What was referred to as Black Forty Seven?

24. What name was given to the secret, anti-European terrorist movent which agitated the Kikuyu tribe of Kenya during the years 1953–57?

25. What was the name of the reform programme introduced into the United States in the 1930s to combat the Great Depression?

26. What name was given to the international agreement regulating the treatment of the wounded in war which was reached at a conference held in 1864?

27. What did the Falstead Act of the 1920s in the USA seek to control?

28. Who was the last Viceroy of India and in which year did India gain her independence?

29. Who was the chief figure in the '26th of July' movement?

30. Napoleon had connections with three islands. He was imprisoned on Elba and died on St Helena – where was he born?

31. Name the two Japanese cities devastated by nuclear bombs in August 1945.

32. Which city hosted the World's Fair *Expo '67* and the 1976 Olympics?

33. In what part of the world was the terrorist organisation EOKA, led by Colonel George Grivas, active in the late 1950s?

34. What nationality was Adolf Hitler?

35. What was the name of the village of west Bengal, India, which was the scene of Clive's victory over the Nawab which gave the British control of Bengal?

36. What famous meeting took place in Ujiji in 1871?

37. Which position did Winston Churchill hold during the First World War?

38. What name was given to the workers who, fearing the loss of their jobs due to the introduction of machinery, rioted and wrecked factories during the period 1811 to 1816?

39. Who were known as The Forty-niners?
40. In a drive to create a great Italian Empire, which country did Mussolini invade in 1935?
41. By what name was Sir Arthur Wellesley more commonly known?
42. On 15th April 1912 over 1000 lives were lost in one dramatic and disastrous accident – what happened?
43. Which Acts were repealed in 1824 and thus stimulated the trade union movement in Britain?
44. Over which country did King Zog rule until expelled by the Italians in 1939?
45. What was the name of the Act by which suffragettes who had been released from prison while on hunger strike, were re-arrested as soon as they regained their strength?
46. What happened in the Welsh village of Aberfan in 1966?
47. What was the name of the peace treaty at the end of World War I?

Inventions

1. What did Sir Humphry Davy invent in the early 19th century?
2. What did the British inventor Sir Christopher Cockerell invent and develop?
3. With which invention of 1783 do you associate the names Jacques and Joseph Montgolfier?
4. Give the year (within ten years) of the first successful parachute jump by André Garnerin.
5. Which invention of 1876 do you associate with the name Melville R Bissel of the United States?

6. What was the name of the train designed and driven by George Stephenson which made its first journey in public passenger service on 27th September 1825?

7. In what sphere did Louis Daguerre make such advances, in the early 19th century, that he gave the word 'daguerrotype' to the English language?

8. Nobel is famous for the endowment he left for the furthering of the cause of humanity, but for what invention is he also remembered?

9. What did the American Whitcomb Judson invent in 1892?

10. For which invention of 1801 is the Italian Pellegrine Tarri credited?

11. A C W Aldis invented a special kind of lamp. For what was this lamp used?

12. In what year were roller skates invented?

13. What did the American Walter Hunt invent?

14. Thomas Edison made the first recording of sound on 6th December 1877 on his 'talking machine'. What were the first words recorded?

15. Auguste Lumière and Louis Lumière developed and pioneered an invention which was to become popular worldwide. Their invention was first seen in public in 1895. What was it?

16. It was first publicly demonstrated by its inventor on 27th January 1926 at 22 Frith Street in London. Before its inventor died in 1946 it had already shown signs of revolutionising society – what was it?

17. For which invention of 1852 is Elisha G Otis credited?

18. What did the American Hamilton Smith invent in 1858?

19. Which pistol took its name from the person who patented it in 1835?

20. They first appeared beside the roads outside the Houses of Parliament in 1868 to assist MPs and came into widespread use in London in 1926. Since then they have become a worldwide feature. What are they?

21. With which invention is William Le Baron Jenny of the USA credited?
22. What name was given to the underwater explosive missile first developed by Robert Whitehead in 1866?
23. It was a technique of generating sound waves of a very high frequency to detect sub-marine objects and was perfected in World War II. It was called the Sound Navigation and Ranging System. By what name was it more familiarly known?
24. Ginger ale and the pneumatic tyre were both invented in the same city. Which city was this?

Inventors

1. Who invented the match? (He lived in the North East of England.)
2. Who was the first man to send a Radio Telegraph signal across the Atlantic Ocean?
3. What was the name of the American who invented the Kodak camera in 1888?
4. Which inventor is accredited with the discovery of both the electric lamp and the gramophone?
5. Which American inventor discovered the lightning conductor and made the first pair of bi-focal spectacles?
6. He was a British inventor and scientist whose many designs included the R100 Airship, the Wellington Bomber, the Swing-Wing Aircraft and the Bouncing Bomb. Who was he?
7. Who was the inventor of the Spinning Mule (1779) which substituted machinery for hand work?
8. Which German invented the mercury thermometer in 1714?

9. Which Englishman invented the jet engine?
10. Who invented traveller's cheques?
11. Who invented the vacuum cleaner?
12. In 1925 an American invented the frozen food process. Who was he?
13. In 1942 he assisted in the design and development of the diving device known as the aqualung. Who was he?
14. Who discovered X-rays in 1895?
15. Which Englishman invented the lathe in 1800?
16. Who devised the first ball-point pen in 1938?
17. Who was the Greek scientist who invented a device to raise water from one level to another?
18. What is the name of the Scot who invented the blast furnace in 1828?
19. Which American invented vulcanised rubber?
20. In 1888 the world's first standard retail petrol car marked the beginning of the motor industry. Who invented the 1½ horsepower car?
21. Which inventor became the father of the hydrogen bomb?
22. Who was the founder of the first English printing press?
23. Who was the Scottish scientist who invented the kaleidoscope in 1816?
24. Which two brothers do you associate with the invention of the aeroplane?
25. Who was the English inventor of a system of shorthand based on sounds instead of letters?
26. Who was the American inventor of the magnetic telegraph?

Language

1. What French phrase has been adopted into the English language – meaning to be familiar with or conversant with?
2. What name do the Americans give to bilberries?
3. The word 'Bible' is derived from the Greek 'biblion'. What does the word literally mean?
4. What is the meaning of the term caveat emptor?
5. The Spanish word for goodbye is Adios – what does this word literally mean?
6. What is the American word used to describe a large co-operatively owned apartment house?
7. Whom do the Scots refer to as a howdie (or howdy)?
8. What is the French name for the English Channel?
9. In the Greek alphabet A is Alpha. What is D?
10. A menu often contains the words hors d'oeuvre. What does this phrase literally mean?
11. How would you translate the philosophical Latin phrase, cogito ergo sum?
12. What do American children call sweets?
13. How many letters are there in the Slavonic alphabet?
14. What is the meaning of the all-purpose Israeli greeting Shalom?
15. The Indian or Hindu word for bandage was adopted by the British soldiers to describe a type of legging worn especially in World War I. What is the word?
16. What, in Gaeldom, is a philabeg?
17. What do the French mean by the phrase à votre santé?
18. What is the Japanese word for goodbye?

19. What is meant by the Latin phrase compos mentis?
20. What is the Dutch term for land reclaimed from the sea or fresh water?
21. Archimedes reputedly shouted out 'Eureka' whilst having a bath. What does the word mean?
22. What is the antonym or opposite of oriental?
23. What name do the Mexicans give to foreigners – especially Americans?
24. What do the Italians mean by the phrase ben venuto?
25. In Spanish-speaking countries, what name is given to an estate or a plantation with a house?
26. What name is given to the kind of mistake in speech in which a person mixes up the initial sounds of spoken words?
27. What is a German motorway called?
28. In the English language it spouts water and is called a tap. What do Americans call it?
29. What is the name of the Celtic tongue spoken in Brittany?
30. What name is given to an armed Italian policeman?
31. What is the meaning of the Irish phrase Erin go bragh?
32. In days gone by, if a Scotsman referred to a man as a 'Johnny Ged's Hole' what trade or occupation would he have?
33. What Latin word is used to express the meaning 'word for word'?
34. In America, what is the usual word used to describe a lawyer?
35. What is the meaning of the Latin phrase Deo gratias?
36. In the Braille alphabet combinations of dots are used to represent letters and figures. What is the maximum number of dots used to portray any single letter?
37. What is the Spanish name for a fictional country rich in gold?
38. A French phrase has been adopted into the English language to describe an illusory feeling of having previously experienced something presently happen-

ing. What is the phrase?

39. Adeste fideles are the Latin first words of an ancient hymn – how are they commonly translated?
40. What is the Spanish word which describes a person who takes part in irregular warfare?
41. Which French word describes both the front of a building and an outwardly deceptive appearance?
42. In Britain, the game is known as draughts. By what name is it known in America?

Literary Characters

1. In the book by Baroness Orczy, by what name was Percy Blakeney otherwise known?
2. Who was 'the knight of doleful countenance'?
3. What is the name of the narrator in C P Snow's sequence of novels, *Strangers and Brothers*?
4. What was the name of the fictional detective created by G K Chesterton?
5. Which fictional detective relies on the employment of 'the little grey cells' (his catch phrase)?
6. Which legendary rascal and heartless seducer was created by Gabriel Tellez?
7. Who was the central character in George Orwell's novel *1984*?
8. According to Beatrix Potter, 'Once upon a time there were four little rabbits . . .' What were their names?
9. What was the full name of Rudyard Kipling's Kim?
10. Who was the ship-wrecked character in R L Stevenson's novel *Treasure Island* who confessed, 'Many's the long night I've dreamed of cheese – toasted mostly'?
11. Which fictional character from a children's book said,

'I am a bear of very little brain and long words bother me'?

12. Which fictional character fell asleep in the Catskill Mountains for 20 years?

13. Which character from *Alice's Adventures in Wonderland* was forever crying 'Off with his head!'?

14. In Dickens' novel *Oliver Twist* who was the elderly criminal who taught the street urchins how to rob, steal and pickpocket?

15. What is Adam Bede's profession in the novel of the same name by George Eliot?

16. Which famous literary character was created by the author Georges Simenon?

17. In Rudyard Kipling's *Jungle Book*, Baghera was a black panther – what was Shere Khan?

18. In Swift's *Gulliver's Travels,* what was the name of the race of brutes in human shape whose name became a word in the English language, meaning a degraded or bestial human being?

19. In Dickens' novel *David Copperfield*, who declared that he was 'willing' to marry Peggotty?

20. Which animals become the leaders in George Orwell's satire *Animal Farm*?

21. In Jules Verne's novel *20,000 Leagues under the Sea* who captained the submarine *Nautilus*?

22. Which animal, in the story by Lewis Carroll, faded away until nothing was left but a grin?

23. What kind of creatures are portrayed in the book *Watership Down*?

24. Aramis and Porthos were two of the three musketeers in Alexandre Dumas' famous story. Who was the third?

25. Who was the comic schoolboy hero created in a series of stories by Frank Richards?

26. Which famous children's character was created in a series of books by Michael Bond?

27. In the novel by Henry Williamson, who or what was Tarka?

28. What literary character did Bram Stoker create in a novel dated 1897?

29. What was the name of the young working-class hero looking for social advancement in the novel *Room At The Top*?

30. Who was the fictional detective, known as the female James Bond, who was created by Peter O' Donnell?

31. What was the name of the shipwrecked sailor who settled the war between King Bombo and King Little?

32. Who was the hero of a well-known folk tale called *The Legend of Sleepy Hollow* written by the American author Washington Irving?

33. What is the name of the Uncle who was the story-teller in the tales about Brer Rabbit?

34. Who was the hero of the stories by James Thurber who was given to extravagant day-dreams?

35. Who brought to life the fictional monster created by Mary Shelley, his name being the title of her novel?

36. Name the famous medical man created by A J Cronin.

37. Which Doctor talked to the animals?

Literature : Authors

1. A mathematician named Charles Lutwidge Dodgson wrote children's stories using a different name. What name?

2. He was a naval administrator born in 1633 and is most famous for keeping a daily account of the Great Plague and Great Fire of London. Who was he?

3. Who created *Swallows And Amazons*, the children's classic?

4. Whose stories include those about the dog and his reflection, the fox and the grapes and the lion and the mouse?

5. What was the pen-name of the writer, philosopher and historian, François Marie Arouet (1694–1778)?

6. Which vet brought increased recognition to the North Yorkshire Moors through his vet books?

7. By what name is the popular thriller writer David John Cornwell better known?

8. Which British author assumed, at times, the nick-name 'Boz'?

9. Who was the Russian novelist who was exiled in 1974 after he had exposed to the world the terrible conditions in Soviet Prison Camps?

10. By what name is the author Eric Arthur Blair better known?

11. He was a Scottish author and dramatist who wrote the plays *Dear Brutus*, *Admirable Crichton* and *Peter Pan*. Who was he?

12. Who is said to have been the first English novelist to deal with the detection of crime? His work *The Woman In White* appeared in 1860.

13. Who was the author of *Carrie's War*, the story of the evacuees Carrie and Nick Willow?

14. What was the pen-name of the American Samuel Langhorne Clemens?

Literature : Book Titles

1. Its literal English translation is 'My Struggle'. What title did Adolph Hitler give to his most famous literary work?

2. Name Stephen Knight's controversial study of the secret world of the freemasons.
3. Which book, by Herman Melville, opens with the words, 'Call me Ishmael'?
4. What name was given to the series of novels by John Galsworthy depicting the life of an upper-middle-class family?
5. Name the famous work which was written following the researches of a scientist on the Galapagos Islands and other places.
6. With which book do you associate the words, 'War is Peace/Freedom is Slavery/Ignorance is Strength'?
7. Which classic by Louisa May Alcott was turned into the musical *A Girl Called Jo*?
8. In which famous book would you find the characters Denisov and Dolokhov?
9. What was the title of Anthony Burgess's book (1962) of London terrorised by teenage gangs?
10. Molly Seagrim is a character in which of Fielding's novels?
11. With which book and film do you associate the character Rhett Butler?
12. What was the original title of Jane Austen's novel, *Pride and Prejudice*?
13. Which novel opens with the words, 'Last night I dreamed I went to Manderley again . . .'?
14. With which book do you associate the characters Magwitch and Estella?
15. Which was the last of Thomas Hardy's novels and his most tragic work?
16. Which novel by Charlotte Brontë told of the riots which resulted when machinery was brought into the cotton mills of Yorkshire?
17. What was the title of James Joyce's autobiographical novel?
18. Tony Lumpkin was a character in which of Oliver Goldsmith's works?
19. Sir Winston Churchill wrote only one novel, which

was published in 1900. What was it called?

20. In which of Graham Greene's novels do you meet the young gang leader and killer named Pinkie?

21. In which book do you meet Eloi, the people living in the upper world, who are preyed on by the underworld Morlocks?

22. What is the title of the anti-war novel which states that if a man fights he is crazy and does not have to fight, but if he does not want to fight he is sane and has to fight?

23. In which novel by J B Priestley are Jesiah Oakroyd, Inigo Jollifart and Elizabeth Trant the central characters?

24. The adventures of Becky Sharp are told in which novel by Thackeray?

25. Which of Charles Dickens' novels was left unfinished in 1870?

26. Give the title of the book written by Harriet Beecher Stowe in which she exposed slave conditions in America.

27. *How the Leopard got his Spots* is one of a collection of stories by Rudyard Kipling. What is this collection called?

28. In which novel would you find reference to The Cracks of Doom, Ents and The Black Riders?

29. What is the title of the Jack London novel concerning Bill and Henry who struggle through the frozen Canadian north with a sled and four dogs followed by a starving wolf-pack?

30. Dorothea Brooke is the heroine in which of George Eliot's novels?

31. In which novel, from 1954, do you meet Ralph, Piggy and Jack Merridew, who are marooned on an uninhabited island after a plane crash?

32. What is the popular name given to the annual publication *Genealogical and Heraldic History of the Peerage, Baronetage and Knightage of the United Kingdom*?

33. Which book was the subject of Regina v Penguin Books Ltd in 1960, with the charge of being obscene?
34. Which modern English classic, written by Walter Greenwood, concerned the lives of Harry and Sally Hardcastle?
35. What was the name of Robert Louis Stevenson's last and unfinished novel?
36. Which anti-war novel, turned into a popular film, was one of the most acclaimed books resulting from World War I?

Literature : Children's Books

1. What was the name of the young chimney sweep in Charles Kingsley's *The Water Babies*?
2. What was the name of the yearling filly in the book by Mary O'Hara?
3. What is the name of the girl detective who is featured in the books *The Hidden Staircase*, *The Bungalow Mystery* and *The Secret of the Old Clock*?
4. Snufkin, Fillyjonk and the Snorks were all characters of which series of tales by Tove Jansson?
5. What was the name of the boat on which Captain Pugwash and Tom the cabin boy sailed?
6. What were the names of the children known as 'The Railway Children'?
7. Which horse, in the story by Anna Sewell, began life as Darkie and had several names as he changed owners?
8. In which books about a mischievous boy do you meet the lisping Violet Elizabeth Bott?
9. In *Tales from Toytown*, what type of creatures were Larry and Dennis?

10. What type of creature was John Burningham's Borka?
11. What is the surname of Dora, Oswald, Dickie, Alice, Noel and HO, who appear in Edith Nesbit's books *The Story of the Treasure Seekers* and *The Wouldbe-goods*?
12. Mattie Doolin, Joe Darling and Willie Styles are three characters created by Catherine Cookson. In which area of England did they live?
13. In *What Katy Did*, what caused Katy Carr's injury which led to her spending four years in a wheelchair?
14. In the book *Fantastic Mr Fox*, by Roald Dahl, what are the names of the three farmers against whom Mr Fox pitted his wits so successfully?
15. Which of Biggles' friends dropped his title but reminded others of it by wearing a monacle and using expressions such as 'by gad' and 'old boy'?
16. What is the name of Ivor the Engine's driver?
17. In *Watership Down* what 'gift' or 'affliction' does the rabbit named Fiver possess?
18. What was the name of the homeless orphan whom Mrs Badger found in Thorp Wood and took home with her in the Alison Uttley stories?
19. Who is adopted as an infant into a family of wolves in *The Jungle Book*?
20. What was the name of the cow in *The Magic Roundabout* in such stories as *The Adventures of Dougal*?
21. What was the name of the English spinster who became a witch who could travel back in time in *Bedknobs and Broomsticks*?
22. What was the name of the tank engine created by Reverend Awdry?
23. What was Billy Bunter's middle name?
24. 'Deeds not grunts' is the motto of which pig created by Kenneth Grahame?
25. What was the surname of Frank and Joe in the books by F W Dixon?
26. In which books do you meet Mrs Tiggie Winkle?
27. Where would you find Eeyore and Kanga?

28. Who are the four children who enter the world of Narnia through a wardrobe in *The Lion, the Witch and the Wardrobe*?

29. What were the names of Andy Pandy's two friends?

30. In *Treasure Island* who was engaged as the ship's cook by Squire Trelawney?

31. Whom did Laura Ingalls marry when she was 18 years old in the stories known as *The Little House on the Prairie*?

32. What is the surname of John, Michael and Wendy in the *Peter Pan* story?

33. Who is the central character in *The Wind in the Willows* with a particular love for motor-cars?

34. Can you name the four girls, collectively known as 'the March girls' in Louisa M Alcott's *Little Women*?

35. What is Paddington Bear's favourite food?

36. Roger Hargreaves made a major contribution to children's literature in the 1970s when he created which well-loved characters?

37. Babar the elephant married his cousin and they had three children. Can you name Babar's wife?

38. What was Milly-Molly-Mandy's full name?

39. What was the title which the American boy Cedric Errol inherited from his grandfather, the Earl of Dorincourt, in the story by Frances Hodgson Burnett?

40. Peter the goat boy was the friend of which girl in the popular storybooks?

Literature : General

1. With what type of books do you associate the name of Baedeker?

2. To what popular sport did the 17th century English

writer Isaak Walton dedicate his most memorable book?

3. From which area of Spain was Don Quixote supposed to come?

4. From which disease did the great writer D H Lawrence die in 1930?

5. Name the brother of the famous literary sisters Charlotte, Emily and Anne Brontë.

6. In Steinbeck's *The Grapes of Wrath*, what was the State, flowing with milk and honey, which was their destination?

7. Who wrote, 'Nothing grows in our garden, only washing and babies'?

8. By what name were the authors Kingsley Amis, John Osborne and John Braine collectively known?

9. Who was the illustrator of the *Winnie the Pooh* books?

10. Where, according to Conan Doyle, did Sherlock Holmes live?

11. Which British town has links with Charles Dickens in that Bleak House, now a Dickens museum, was his home for writing *David Copperfield*?

12. What letter is used most often in English language and literature?

13. What was the British author Somerset Maugham's handicap?

14. How did Virginia Woolf die in 1941?

15. According to the Prologue to Chaucer's *The Canterbury Tales*, how many husbands had the wife of Bath?

16. Which moorland was the setting for Blackmore's *Lorna Doone*?

17. Whom did Ben Johnson call 'Sweet Swan of Avon'?

18. Edgar Wallace was one of the most prolific writers of the 20th century. How many books did he write between 1905 and his death in 1932?

19. Who was the great American journalist and news-paper proprietor whose name lives on in his prizes awarded annually to authors?

20. What was the subject matter of Ernest Hemingway's work *The Green Hills of Africa*?

21. What did John Bunyan refer to as 'Celestial City' in his *Pilgrim's Progress*?

22. Which one word describes a narrative in verse or prose with a secondary meaning, usually a moral or spiritual one?

23. Which famous critic and biographer (1880–1932) lived at 51 Gordon Square, London?

24. *The Book of Kells* has been called 'the most beautiful book in the world'. What is the nature of its content?

25. Can you name the English publisher who compiled and published *Peerage of England, Scotland and Ireland* (1802)? Revised editions today still bear his name.

26. Who was the wife who kept her husband in suspense by telling him stories over 1001 nights and thus escaped death, which had been the fate of his previous wives?

27. Which famous author once lived at a place called 'Gad's Hill'?

28. What was Thomas Hardy's profession before he started writing novels?

29. Hablot Knight Browne was the illustrator of *The Pickwick Papers* and other Dickens novels. What was his pseudonym?

30. Where was J R R Tolkein, the author of *The Lord Of The Rings*, born?

31. What term is used for the practice of writing books, articles, etc., for another person, whose name will appear as that of the author?

32. Which famous person in his will left his wife the furniture and his 'second-best bed'?

Literature : Poets & Poetry

1. Who was the first occupant of Poets' Corner in Westminster Abbey?
2. *Songs of Innocence* and *Songs of Experience* were two books of poems by which 18th century poet and artist?
3. Which British poet gained success in 1955 with his volume of poems entitled *The Less Deceived*?
4. To whom was Tennyson's masterpiece *In Memoriam* dedicated?
5. The Gentleman's Magazine, in 1735, published a poem about a devoted old couple. Their names have become synonymous with elderly sweethearts. Who were they?
6. Which talented poet wrote detective stories under the pseudonym Nicholas Blake?
7. Which poet's works include *Easter 1916* and *The Lake Isle of Innisfree*?
8. *A Shropshire Lad* (1896) was one of the pessimistic lyrical poems by which English poet?
9. Who wrote the following lines:
   'Theirs not to make reply,
   Theirs not to reason why,
   Theirs but to do and die'?
10. Who was the English poet known for *To his Coy Mistress*, *The Garden* and *The Definition of Love*?
11. 'I wandered lonely as a cloud/That floats on high o'er vales and hills', are the opening lines of which poem?
12. Who was the heroine of Pope's poem *The Rape of the Lock*?

13. Who wrote an account of her own nervous breakdown in fictionalised form in *The Bell Jar* (1971), though is more commonly known for her poetry?

14. Which literary giant wrote the oft-quoted lines –
'O young Lochinvar is come out of the west,
Through all the wide Border, his steed was the best'?

15. Who wrote a famous book of poems for children called *Old Possum's Book Of Practical Cats*?

16. Who was the American Poet and critic who was the author of *Tales of Mystery And Imagination*?

17. Which British author wrote the volumes of verse called *When We Were Very Young* (1924) and *Now We Are Six* (1927)?

18. 'I weep for Adonais – he is dead!' is the opening line of a poem by Shelley that is an elegy to which other writer?

19. In *The Rime of the Ancient Mariner*, Coleridge told of the bad luck which came to those who killed which bird?

20. Who was known by the nickname The Ayrshire Poet?

21. Which British artist and humorist popularised the limerick in his *Book of Nonsense* (1946)?

22. The biography entitled *The Stricken Deer* was written by Lord David Cecil. The life of which poet did it portray?

23. Which poet's works include *The Earth Compels* (1938), *Autumn Journal* (1939) and *Plant and Phantom* (1941)?

24. Which English poet's works include *Ode To Duty*, *Intimations of Immortality* and *Michael*?

25. Who were named The Lake Poets?

26. Which three poets were collectively known as The Liverpool Poets?

27. Who was nicknamed The Water Poet?

28. The *Barretts of Wimpole Street* tells the story of a love affair between two poets. Elizabeth Barrett was one – who was her lover?

29. According to the narrative poem, where would you

find a 'green-eyed yellow idol'?

30. Which Scottish poet was known as The Ettrick Shepherd?

31. According to the poet, where did Kublai Khan decree his stately pleasure dome?

32. Which English poet was drowned whilst sailing off the coast of Italy in 1822?

33. What, according to the poet Browning, 'split open the kegs of salted sprats, made nests inside men's Sunday hats'?

34. Which English poet of Huguenot descent wrote *Songs of Childhood* (1902) under the pseudonym Walter Ramal?

35. What was the pen-name of the Irish poet George William Russell?

36. He was a young English poet – killed in the First World War at the age of twenty-eight – who wrote amongst other sonnets one entitled *The Soldier*. Who was he?

37. What is the bird which aroused Wordsworth to question whether it could be a bird 'or but a wandering voice'?

38. To what was Burns referring when he opened his poem with the line: 'Wee, sleekit, cow'rin, tim'rous beastie'?

Literature : Shakespeare

1. What was the name of the ghost who haunted the guilty usurper Macbeth?

2. What is the name of the king of the fairies – he appeared in Shakespeare's *A Midsummer Night's Dream*?

3. Which Shakespearean character has the largest speaking part?

4. Who was the fat, convivial, good-humoured braggart in Shakespeare's *Henry IV* and *The Merry Wives of Windsor*?
5. According to Shakespeare, Caliban was a 'savage and deformed slave'. In which play did he appear?
6. Which of Shakespeare's plays begins with the following words: 'If music be the food of love, play on. Give me excess of it'?
7. The Forest of Arden is the scene of which of Shakespeare's plays?
8. In the Shakespearean tragedy *Julius Caesar*, what are the names of the wives of Caesar and Brutus?
9. Who, according to Shakespeare, said: 'A horse, a horse. My Kingdom for a horse'?
10. Which Shakespearean play is set in Sicilia and Bohemia?
11. Hamlet and Macbeth are two of Shakespeare's great tragedies. Name the other two.
12. If we accept Shakespeare's version, in what battle were 10,000 Frenchmen killed and only 29 Englishmen?
13. Which Shakespeare play has a title which is a proverb?
14. Who spoke the 'Seven Ages of Man' speech which began, 'All the world's a stage, and all the men and women merely players . . .'?
15. In *Anthony and Cleopatra*, what was the name of Caesar's sister, who was also Anthony's wife?
16. What do Shakespeare's *The Tempest*, Milton's *Paradise Lost* and Pope's *The Rape of the Lock* have in common?
17. Who was the youngest of King Lear's daughters and the only one who loved him?
18. Name the villain in the play *Othello*.
19. From which Shakespearean play are these lines taken: 'Life's but a walking shadow – a poor player that struts and frets his hour upon the stage and then is heard no more'?
20. Which Shakespearean play should ideally be performed on the 23rd June?

21. Pericles was the Prince of which country?
22. What was another name for Puck in *A Midsummer Night's Dream*?
23. From which of Shakespeare's plays comes the line, 'A young man married is a man that's marred'?
24. What is the full title of Shakespeare's play commonly known as 'Hamlet'?
25. What was the name of the character who was the brother of the King of Naples in *The Tempest* and brother of Viola in *Twelfth Night*?
26. What was the name of the rich Jew in *The Merchant of Venice*?
27. What was the relationship between Shakespeare's characters Othello and Desdemona?
28. Can you name the shrew in the play *The Taming of the Shrew*?
29. 'Two households, both alike in dignity . . .' is the opening line of which Shakespearean play?
30. How did Ophelia die in *Hamlet*?
31. Can you name the court jester in *As You Like It*?
32. What was the name of Desdemona's father in *Othello*?
33. Which Shakespearean play begins on a ship at sea in the middle of a storm?
34. What was the name of Shylock's daughter in *The Merchant of Venice*?
35. What title is held by Shakespeare's Cymbeline?

Literature : Who Wrote?

1. Who wrote the following children's stories: *The Ugly Duckling*, *The Tinderbox* and *The Emperor's New Clothes*?

2. Who is remembered for his ever-popular work *Three Men In A Boat*?

3. *Goodbye Mr Chips* told the story of the life of a shy schoolmaster from his first job until his death. Who wrote this book?

4. Which knight wrote the book *Heart of the Antarctic*?

5. Who wrote the novel *The Magus*?

6. Which English dramatist is best known for his early play *'Tis Pity She's a Whore*?

7. Whose autobiographical novel is entitled *The Way Of All Flesh*?

8. Which Russian novelist, sent to hard labour in Siberia, was the author of *Crime And Punishment* and *The Idiot*?

9. Who wrote the celebrated trilogy of country life in the 1880s entitled *Lark Rise*, *Over To Candleford* and *Candleford Green*?

10. Whose books included *The Would-Be-Goods*, *Five Children and It* and *The Phoenix and the Carpet*?

11. Which author of modern times wrote *Ulysses*?

12. Who wrote *Rage of Angels* and *Master Of The Game*?

13. Who challenged the traditional roles of women in her book *The Second Sex*?

14. Who wrote about a vulnerable young actress who finds herself a pawn in the Arab-Israeli conflict in *The Little Drummer Girl*?

15. Which Scottish male chauvinist and religious reformer wrote, amongst other things, a work entitled *The First Blast of the Trumpet Against the Monstrous Regiment of Women* in 1558?

16. Which American novelist and Nobel prize winner (1949) wrote *The Sound And The Fury*, *As I Lay Dying* and *Sanctuary*?

17. Which author do you associate with the works, *Decline and Fall*, *A Handful of Dust* and *Put Out More Flags*?

18. Which English novelist was the author of *Mary Barton*, *Cranford* and *The Life of Charlotte Brontë*?

19. Whose works include *Tristram Shandy* and *A Sentimental Journey*?
20. Whose novels include *Lord Jim* and *Nostromo*?
21. Who wrote the cartoon book *The Snowman*?
22. What is the name of the American historical novelist who wrote the book entitled *The Last of the Mohicans*?
23. Who wrote the books *Princess Daisy*, *Scruples* and *Mistral's Daughter*?
24. Which author wrote *Clayhanger*?
25. Who wrote *The Female Eunuch*?
26. Which 19th century writer wrote *The Picture of Dorian Gray*, *Lady Windermere's Fan* and *The Importance of Being Earnest*?
27. Which author do you associate with the novel *Penmarric*?
28. Which best-selling author wrote, *The Devil's Alternative*, *The Dogs of War* and *The Odessa File*?
29. Who wrote *The Day Of The Triffids*?
30. Which French Romantic novelist wrote *The Count of Monte Cristo*?
31. Who took four years to write her famous book entitled *Household Management*?
32. Which English author, known for her detective novels, wrote the religious radio play *The Man Born To Be King*?
33. Who wrote *A Testament Of Youth*?
34. Who wrote about her childhood in Africa in *The Flame Trees of Thika*?
35. Which novelist and poet's first novel was *Henry Brocken*?
36. Which author wrote *Tom Brown's Schooldays*?
37. Who wrote the detective story *The Red House Mystery*?
38. Who wrote *Jacob's Room* and *Orlando*?
39. Who was the young American inspired by Alhambra in Spain who wrote the famous *Tales of Alhambra*?
40. Who wrote *Love for Lydia* and *Day's End*?
41. Which 18th century Scottish author wrote about

Roderick Random, *Peregrine Pickle* and *Humphrey Clinker*?

42. Who wrote *20,000 Leagues under the Sea*?
43. Who wrote the novel *The Call Of The Wild*?
44. Which English historian and author wrote *The Decline and Fall of the Roman Empire*?
45. Who wrote the novel *Gentlemen Prefer Blondes*?
46. Who wrote *The Prime of Miss Jean Brodie*, the story of a headstrong schoolteacher in the thirties?
47. Whose works include *Daisy Miller* and *The Portrait Of A Lady*?
48. Which Irish novelist's works include *Castle Rackrent*, *The Absentee* and *Belinda*?
49. Name the English novelist, poet and architect who was responsible for such works as *The Mayor of Casterbridge*, *Tess of the D'Urbervilles* and the dramatic poem *The Dynasts*.
50. Who described how he escaped when he was a prisoner in South Africa during the Boer War in his autobiography, *My Early Life*?
51. Which English novelist and journalist wrote *The Heart Of The Matter* and *Our Man In Havana*?
52. Which playwright's autobiographical *Borstal Boy* describes his formative years in the IRA?
53. Which writer became an instant success with his first novel *Not a Penny More, Not a Penny Less*?
54. Which author do you associate with the novel *The History of Mr Polly*?
55. Which British naval officer wrote the series of boys' books which included *Children of the New Forest*?
56. Who wrote the book *An Unsuitable Job For A Woman*?
57. Which English 17th Century writer's most famous works are entitled *Paradise Lost* and *Paradise Regained*?
58. Who was the American author of *Billy Budd* and *Moby Dick*?

59. Who wrote the story of *The Squirrel, the Hare and the Little Grey Rabbit*?
60. Who wrote *Alice in Wonderland*?

London

1. By what name is the New Palace of Westminster more commonly known?
2. On London Underground maps, which line is always represented by the colour yellow?
3. Where would you find the famous Whispering Gallery?
4. The Pearly Kings and Queens are the most famous inhabitants of which part of London?
5. On which London street do you find the Prime Minister's official residence?
6. In which London square would you find two memorials to the great Indian leader, Mahatma Gandhi?
7. What is the name of the famous cheese shop in Jermyn Street, London?
8. Name the nearest seaside resort to London.
9. Which London street is named after a fictional French émigré from Charles Dickens' novel, *A Tale of Two Cities*?
10. Name London's largest meat market which is also the largest covered-in market in the world.
11. Which London cemetery is famous as the resting place of Thackeray, Trollope, Cruickshank, Cardinal Manning and Wilkie Collins?
12. Which London street was the site of a former leper colony?

13. Where and what is Rotten Row?
14. Which London thoroughfare has been referred to as 'the hub of the British Empire'?
15. What is known as the Upper House?
16. Which famous London street was formerly known as Tyburn Way?
17. What nickname is given to the London underground?
18. Which famous London street is associated with the medical profession?
19. What is known as the Old Lady of Threadneedle Street?
20. What was the name of the tavern in Bread Street, London, which was the meeting place of the Friday Street Club founded by Sir Walter Raleigh and frequented by Shakespeare and Ben Jonson?
21. In which London gardens would you find the Merchant Navy Memorial to the men and ships lost during the Second World War?
22. What is the name of the parish church of Buckingham Palace where George I was church warden?
23. By what name is the Central Criminal Court in London most popularly known?
24. Why is Portobello Road in London so named?
25. In which half-timbered London building would you find Prince Henry's Room?
26. By what other name is Grosvenor Square in London known?
27. Which London street became famous in the 1960s as a fashion centre?
28. Which London street is associated with the film industry?
29. Why is Sloane Square in London so named?

Mathematics

1. What is the name of the branch of mathematics which deals with relations between sides and angles of triangles?
2. The binary system of numbers uses only two numerals, what are they?
3. In geometry, what do we call a straight line that touches a curve at one point but does not cut it?
4. In Roman numerals what does LXX stand for?
5. What is the mathematical term which means without end or limitless?
6. How many sides has a dodecagon?
7. If a clock in a mirror says twenty to three, what time is it?
8. What do the numbers 2,3,5,7,11,13,17,19 and 23 have in common?
9. Which Scottish mathematician invented logarithms?
10. What descriptive mathematical term is used to describe the six-sided cells of a honeycomb?
11. The symbol Pi is used in mathematics – can you give its value to three decimal places?
12. If, during a mathematical conversion, you used the formula – subtract 32, multiply by 5 and divide by 9 – what conversion would you be doing?

Medical Matters : General

1. Which instrument is used to measure the temperature of bodies?
2. If a doctor carried out a tracheotomy, on which part of the body would he operate?
3. Which branch of medicine is concerned with ailments specific to women, especially those of the reproductive system?
4. What is the name of the method of treating injury and illness by physical means such as massage and exercise?
5. What would a doctor be trying to find out if he gave you the Ishihara Test?
6. In medicine, with what is dermatology concerned?
7. What is the name of the English medical journal established in 1823 by Dr Wakley?
8. Which theory (now discredited) proposed that a person's mental development could be measured by an examination of the skull?
9. What name is given to the Chinese practice of alleviating pain and treating disease by inserting needles at various points in the skin?
10. From which plant do we obtain the drug belladonna?
11. In medical terms, what is the study of children's diseases?
12. What is the medical name given to the study of a wide range of diseases of the brain or the nervous system?
13. Lentigines is the medical term for them. What are they?
14. What is novocain widely used as?
15. What is the name of the oath which is sworn at some

medical schools on the occasion of taking a degree?

16. What did William Harvey discover about the human body in the early 17th century?
17. What is the name of a fracture where the tissues of the body are torn and the bone is exposed to the open air?
18. What name is given to the surgical removal of the womb?
19. Lassa Fever was first detected in 1969 near the village of Lassa. In which country is Lassa?
20. Which branch of medicine and biology deals with the functioning of the healthy human body?
21. Why did the South African Louis Washkansky achieve world-wide fame in 1967?
22. What drug is obtained from the cinchona tree?

Medical Matters :
The Human Body

1. What is the average human body temperature in degrees centigrade?
2. There are four principal types of teeth. Name them.
3. Give the approximate weight (in pounds) of the human brain.
4. The chromosome is the microscopic thread-like body of cells which carries hereditary factors or genes. What is the normal number of chromosomes a human being has?
5. What is the fontanelle?
6. Human skin has two distinct layers. What are they called?
7. What are the four main blood groups?
8. It is a bone of the body with the medical name

'sternum'. What is it?

9. Where in the human body is the umbilicus?
10. What is the name of the hormone which controls the supply of sugar from the blood to the muscles?
11. On which part of the body would you find the bridge?
12. Where in the body would you find carpals and phalanges?
13. What is the name of the chief muscle, used in breathing, which separates the chest from the abdomen?
14. Where would you find the malleus, incus and stapes?
15. Where in the body would you find the epiglottis?
16. Name the three long bones in the arm.
17. What is the average number of heartbeats per minute of an adult human heart under normal conditions?
18. How many pairs of ribs has man?
19. What is the longest bone in the human body?
20. What is the more common name for the patella?
21. To the nearest 10, how many bones are there in the human body?
22. How many teeth are there in a full adult set?
23. What is the name of the bitter yellow-brown fluid secreted by the liver?
24. Which carry blood to the heart, arteries or veins?
25. Where in the body would you find the pulmonary artery?
26. What is the other name for the scapula?
27. What is the name of the clear yellowish liquid which separates from blood after clotting?
28. Where is the jugular vein?
29. Name the fibrous tissue which binds bones together.
30. Where in the human body would you find the metatarsals?
31. How many bones are there in the skull?
32. What is the name of the coloured part of the eye which surrounds the pupil?
33. By what common names are the maxilla and mandible known?

Medical Matters :
Medical Conditions

1. If you were suffering from calvities what would be wrong with you?
2. What is dyspepsia more commonly known as?
3. Which organ of the body is inflamed in nephritis?
4. If you were suffering from hepatitis which part of the body would be most affected?
5. What form of illness caused the Black Death in the 14th century?
6. What name is given to pain and aching in the lower back?
7. What name is given to the disease of the eye in which the lens becomes opaque causing partial or total blindness?
8. What name is given to the medical condition of a deficiency in the amount of red pigment haemoglobin in the blood?
9. If you suffered from *Mal de Mer* what would be your problem?
10. What is the name of the disease caused by the lack of vitamin C?
11. Which disease causes a serious form of pneumonia? The germ appears to have a liking for hot water or air conditioning systems in large institutions such as hospitals or hotels.
12. Which organ of the body is affected by Bright's Disease?
13. What is the medical name given to the disorder which

mainly affects young girls aged 14–17 years who lose weight to the extent of emaciation?

14. Which parts of the body are most commonly affected by chilblains?

15. What name is given to twins who are joined together by some part of their anatomy?

16. Which vitamin deficiency causes rickets?

17. Which tropical disease is transmitted by the mosquito bite?

18. What is the medical name given to the condition of word blindness – that is, difficulty in understanding the written word?

19. Sleeping Sickness is an infectious disease of tropical Africa which is transmitted by which fly?

20. If a person had a prosthesis, what would he possess?

21. Which part of the body is affected by conjunctivitis?

22. At which stage of life are people more prone to Alzheimers disease?

23. In colour blindness, which two colours are most commonly confused?

24. Pertussis is an infectious disease which usually attacks children. By what name is it more commonly known?

25. What is the layman's name for varicella, one of the commonest infectious diseases?

26. What is the medical name for German measles?

27. What name is given to the infection of the gums which causes the edges of the tooth sockets to bleed easily when the teeth are brushed?

28. What part of the body is affected by astigmatism?

29. Epidemic parotitis is the technical name for which common disease?

30. What is the common name for the disease called trismus – a form of tetanus?

31. Epistaxis is the technical name for which common complaint?

32. What is the medical terminology to describe a person who has an abnormal preoccupation with their real or imagined illnesses?

33. What name is given to the sudden and complete loss of memory?
34. Which part of the body is affected by encephalitis?
35. What is the medical name for mongolism?
36. What is the common name for halitosis?
37. Which part of the body may suffer from ophthalmia?
38. What is the name for the condition of the mind that leads to an irresistible tendency to steal things?
39. What is the common name for toxaemia?
40. What is the common name for enuresis?

Money

1. Which British gold coin was introduced by Henry VII and became worth a pound in 1817?
2. In what year was Decimal Currency introduced in the United Kingdom?
3. Which Old English coin was equal to four pence?
4. What is the French phrase used to describe an office which deals in the exchange of currency?
5. How many cents make up an American dime?
6. We often hear of the Chancellor of the Exchequer. How did the word 'exchequer' come into being?
7. In world finance, what do the initials IMF represent?
8. How many old pennies were there in one guinea?
9. On the stock exchange, what name was given to the person who sold shares in the expectation that prices would fall?
10. What is the American equivalent of the Financial Times Index?
11. The Royal Mint issued a special 50p piece to celebrate Britain's entry into the European Economic Com-

munity. What was the design on the reverse side?

12. What was the popular name for the group of Swiss bankers thought by Harold Wilson to influence world finance?

13. Our silver coins are no longer made of silver. What two metals are they made of?

14. In discussion about the country's economy, reference is often made to GNP – what do these initials stand for?

15. What is the French equivalent of the Stock Exchange?

16. Which of the pre-decimalisation coins of Britain portrayed a portcullis on its reverse side?

17. Which coin was known as a bob?

Mottoes

1. Whose motto is 'Let not the deep swallow me up'?

2. Which individual has the motto 'Ich Dien' or 'I Serve'?

3. What is the unofficial motto of the Royal Canadian Mounted Police?

4. Which English department store has the slogan 'never knowingly undersold'?

5. Whose motto is 'per ardua ad astra'?

6. What is the motto of the Special Air Services – SAS?

7. What is the motto of the US Federal Bureau of Investigation based on its initials FBI?

8. What was the official motto of the French Republic, adopted in 1793?

9. Which organisation's badge – or insignia – bears the inscription 'Blood and Fire'?

10. What was the motto of the Three Musketeers?

Music : Composers

1. Who composed *The Rite Of Spring*, *The Firebird* and *Petruska*?
2. Which US jazz pianist, composer and bandleader do you associate with *Mood Indigo* and *I Got It Bad*?
3. The *Magnificat*, *Mass in B Minor* and *Easter Oratorio* are all works by which composer?
4. Who wrote the four anthems known as *Coronation Anthems* for the coronation of George II in Westminster Abbey?
5. How many symphonies did Beethoven write?
6. In 1919 a world famous pianist and composer was elected the first Prime Minister of Poland. What was his name?
7. He was a German composer who lived between the years 1854–1921. His name was later 'borrowed' by a popular singer. Who was he?
8. Who wrote *A German Requiem* in memory of his mother?
9. *On Hearing the First Cuckoo in Spring* is one of the best known orchestral works of which English composer?
10. Who composed the *Peer Gynt* Suite?
11. Which composer wrote the works entitled *Hungarian Rhapsodies*?
12. *Claire de Lune* was one of the most popular piano pieces by which composer?
13. The *Symphonie Fantastique* is the most popular work of which French composer?

14. Which British playwright and composer, who died in 1973, wrote *Mad Dogs and Englishmen go out in the Midday Sun* and *Don't put your Daughter on the Stage Mrs Worthington*?

15. Which American pianist, composer and conductor do you associate with *On the Town* and *West Side Story*?

16. Who composed his *New World* symphony in New York while he was head of the National Conservatoire there?

17. The theme music to the film *The Graduate* starring Dustin Hoffman was entitled *Mrs Robinson*. Who wrote and performed the song?

18. How would the music of the composers Vivaldi, Purcell and Handel be classified?

19. In 1740 Henry Carey was attributed with the composition and singing of a famous musical work. What was it?

20. Which English composer's oratorios include *The Kingdom* and *The Dream Of Gerontius*?

21. What nationality was the composer Bartók?

22. Which world famous American composer, who died in 1937, wrote *Swanee*, *I Got Rhythm* and *Rhapsody in Blue*?

23. Which composer has been called 'the poet of the piano' because of the originality and delicacy of his playing?

24. Who was the Russian composer of the well-known *Leningrad Symphony (No. 7)*?

25. Name the French composer who was the founder of the French Grand Opera.

26. Who was the pioneer of 'ragtime' and jazz music in America? His musicals include *Annie Get Your Gun* and *Call Me Madam*.

27. Who composed the ballet *Sleeping Beauty*?

28. Who composed the *Pastoral* and *Eroica* symphonies?

29. Who was the amateur musician who composed *Pictures From An Exhibition*?

30. Can you name the American song-writer who com-

142

posed the popular operetta *Show Boat* which includes the song *Ol' Man River*?

31. Which court composer do you associate with *Judas Maccabaeus*?

32. Who was the English composer of the song *Onward Christian Soldiers*?

33. Which successful American composer was named The March King?

34. Name the Russian composer whose works include the opera *Love for Three Oranges* and the fairy tale *Peter and the Wolf*.

35. Which famous musical duo wrote the music and lyrics for the film *The Sound of Music*?

36. Which composer lived between 1874 and 1934 and created the orchestral suite *The Planets* and the choral *Hymn of Jesus*?

Music : General

1. What is the nickname of Haydn's *Symphony No. 101 in D major*?

2. Who was the first American musical director of the New York Philharmonic Orchestra?

3. Who said, 'If you have to ask what jazz is, you'll never know'?

4. What famous 20th century British singer was originally christened Harry Webb?

5. Which festival associated with Shaw and Elgar was revived in 1977 in an inland resort in Hereford and Worcester?

6. Who was the English conductor who began the Promenade Concerts in London in 1895 and con-

ducted them until his death?

7. In which famous musical are Sky Masterson, a gambler and city slicker, and Sarah Brown, the Mission lass, two central characters?

8. What was the name of the night club in Liverpool in which the Beatles and other 'pop' groups started their careers in the early Sixties?

9. Which American pop star said, 'I don't know anything about music. In my line you don't have to'?

10. What is the title of the French National Anthem?

11. Glen Miller was the leader of the most popular dance band in World War II. What was the title of his signature tune?

12. What city in South Carolina, USA, gave its name to a lively dance in the early 20th century?

13. What was the name of the Beatles' first hit record?

14. When he was young he had an accident in which his hands were crushed and he was told that he would never play the piano again. He overcame this tragedy with years of perseverance and practice and became the king of pre-Elvis rock. Who was he?

15. From which of Tchaikovsky's ballets comes *The Dance of the Sugar Plum Fairy*?

16. What type of dance do you associate with the music *Tales From The Vienna Woods*?

17. What is the alternative nickname of Haydn's *Lamentation Symphony*?

18. Who was the famous medical missionary who toured Europe giving recitals of Bach's organ works?

19. By what nickname was Louis Armstrong known?

20. Which singer who sold 100 million discs released her autobiography *Who's Sorry Now?* in 1985?

21. The capital city of the state of Tennessee is noted for its contribution to American music. What is it?

22. Robert Zimmerman became a popular and sometimes controversial singer in the 1960s. By what name is he better known?

23. What is the popular name for Beethoven's symphony

No. 9 in D minor?

24. Her married name was Madame Johanna Maria Goldschmidt and she was born in Sweden in 1820. She died in 1887, having become one of the finest soprano singers of her time. By what name was she better known?

25. Give the nationality of the world famous violinist Yehudi Menuhin.

26. He organised his first jazz band in 1936 and continued as band leader for over 45 years. In films he only appeared with the orchestra, but these include *Jamboree* in 1957 and *Blazing Saddles* in 1974. Give his name.

Music : Instruments

1. Which instrument in an orchestra produces the deepest sound among all the brass instruments?
2. How many strings has a cello?
3. Which musical instrument do you associate with Richard Clayderman?
4. Which instrument is traditionally regarded as the national instrument of Scotland?
5. Name the percussion instrument consisting of a pair of shell-shaped wooden blocks which are characteristic to Spain.
6. Name the four families of instruments which comprise a modern symphony orchestra.
7. Which instrument was invented by Johann Christoph Denner around 1690 but did not come into general use until Mozart wrote a concerto for it?
8. Who made the famous violins of Cremona?

9. What is the smallest size of grand piano?
10. What is the full name of the instrument usually called a 'cello'?
11. With what musical instrument do you associate the musician Larry Adler?
12. What is the name of the triangular guitar of Tartar origin very popular among Russian peasantry?
13. What is the name of the ancient greek stringed instrument which resembles a small harp but is played with a plectrum?
14. Name the principal instrument in a brass band.
15. Name the four instruments in the brass section of the orchestra.
16. Which instrument do you associate with the musician Julian Lloyd Webber?
17. Which musical instrument does this describe: 'a large brass wind instrument having a tube which is adjusted in length for different notes'?
18. Name the largest member of the violin family.
19. To which section of the orchestra does the piccolo belong?
20. How many keys are there on a standard piano keyboard?
21. With which musical instrument do you associate Dizzy Gillespie?
22. With which musical instrument is the musician James Galway associated?
23. Name the low-pitched brass instrument with four valves, used in brass bands.
24. With which instrument was the great Italian musician Nicolo Paganini associated?
25. Rodrigo composed his *Concerto d'Aranjuez* for which instrument?
26. Name the Spanish cellist and conductor who founded the Barcelona Orchestra (1919) and raised the status of the cello to a solo instrument.

Music : Opera

1. Who wrote the opera *Madame Butterfly*?
2. Escamillo is the bullfighter in which opera by Bizet?
3. Whose final opera was called *Death in Venice*?
4. Which British contralto had the title role of Britten's *The Rape of Lucretia* written for her?
5. What is another name for the character Figaro?
6. What is the name of the only opera composed by Beethoven?
7. Which English mezzo-soprano created the role of Auntie in Britten's *Peter Grimes*?
8. Who composed the opera *The Gambler* which was based on a Dostoyevsky story?
9. *Duke Bluebeard's Castle* is an opera by which composer?
10. George Gershwin wrote the music for a folk opera in which the cast were all negro. What is its name?
11. Which Swiss hero was the subject of an opera by Rossini?
12. Benjamin Britten composed an opera which he titled *Gloriana* to commemorate an important historical event. What was the event?
13. Which German composer wrote the opera entitled *Hansel And Gretel*?
14. Who wrote the opera *The Flying Dutchman* which was first performed in 1843?
15. Who wrote the opera *The Girl of the Golden West*?
16. Who composed the opera *Cosi fan tutte* and what is the translation of this phrase?
17. Who wrote the opera entitled *The Fair Maid of Perth*?

18. Name the Russian composer of the opera *Boris Godunov*.
19. Helen Porter Mitchell, better known as Dame Nellie Melba, was a famous opera singer who died in 1931. What nationality was she?
20. Where is the La Scala Opera House?
21. *Die Zauberflöte* is a famous opera by Mozart. What is its meaning in translation?

Musical Terms

1. What is the meaning of the musical term *da capo*?
2. Long before it became a popular operatic piece a 'barcarole' used to be sung by a certain group of people. Who were they?
3. What term describes a prelude for an orchestra before an opera or choral work?
4. Which musical term means in church music style?
5. A full choir is divided into four ranges of voices – can you name them?
6. In music what does the term *allegro* mean?
7. What is the meaning of the musical term *fortissimo*?
8. What is a metronome?
9. What is the name given to the highest adult male voice?
10. What does the musical term *largo* mean?
11. Which musical term is used to describe a vocal solo, usually in opera, often in three sections with the third part being a repeat of the first?
12. What musical term is used to describe a male voice between tenor and bass?
13. What name is given to the stick which the conductor

uses to give directions to the orchestra?

14. In music what does the term *pizzicato* mean?
15. Soprano is the highest female voice – what name is given to the lowest female voice?
16. What name is given to a quartet of amateur male singers who specialize in close-harmony arrangments of popular songs?
17. What is the American slang name which describes the world of popular composers of modern music?

Mythology : Greek & Roman

1. Who, in Greek mythology, destroyed the monsters Python and Cyclops?
2. According to legend, what connection does Pheidippedes have with modern athletics?
3. How did Achilles die?
4. What were the names of the twins who, according to legend, were abandoned and suckled by a she-wolf?
5. Which mythological character, famous for his great beauty, had a son and daughter by Aphrodite?
6. In Greek mythology, who was Apollo's twin sister?
7. Who was the wife of Zeus and goddess of marriage?
8. In Greek mythology, who stole fire from the gods and gave it to mankind?
9. Pax is the Roman goddess of what?
10. Name the king of Sparta who was the husband of Helen of Troy.
11. What was the name of the Greek mountain consecrated to the Muses?
12. In Greek mythology, who was the son of Daedalus who died when his wings melted when he flew too

close to the sun?

13. Name the goat-legged Greek god who presided over the flocks.

14. The word 'cereal' comes from the name of the Roman goddess of corn and harvest. Who was this goddess?

15. By what collective name are Stheno, Euryale and Medusa known?

16. Who, in Greek mythology, was the forsaken lover of Cressida?

17. Who was the great musician of Greek legend who went into Hades in search of his dead wife Eurydice?

18. Who was the Roman goddess of dawn?

19. Atalanta, in Greek mythology, was a huntress. What attribute made her famous?

20. According to the Greek mythologians, Argus had 100 eyes. When he was slain by Hermes, to what creature were his eyes transferred by Hera?

21. Which day of the week is named after a Roman god?

22. Which Greek hero was credited with the strategy of using a wooden horse to assist in the raising of the siege of Troy?

23. Name the daughter of Minos of Crete who gave Theseus the thread which enabled him to find his way out of the labyrinth.

24. Name the Greek god of war.

25. Neptune was the Roman King of the oceans but the Greeks had another name for him. What was it?

26. By what creature was the Greek god Adonis wounded?

27. What was the name of the ship in which Jason and the Argonauts sailed in search of the Golden Fleece?

28. What is the Roman name for the father of the gods and king of heaven?

29. Who was the Greek hero of the Trojan War who went mad when Achilles' armour was awarded to Ulysses instead of to him?

30. In Greek mythology, Bellerophon decided to fly to heaven on a winged horse. What was the horse's name?

31. In mythology, what is the Roman god of fire called?
32. Who was the nymph who was changed into a laurel-bush to save her from Apollo?
33. What is the name of the Greek goddess of victory?
34. What was the name of the one-eyed giant in Greek mythology?
35. Who, according to Greek mythology, was so handsome that he fell in love with his own reflection?
36. In Greek legend, which prophetess was the foreteller of doom?
37. What was the name of the two-faced god of doorways and archways who gave his name to a month of the year?
38. In Greek mythology, what was the Sword of Damocles suspended by?
39. He was known as Hermes in Greek mythology and was the messenger of the gods. What name was he given by the Romans?
40. Whom, in Greek mythology, did Zeus punish by making him support the heavens with his head and his hands?
41. What was the name of the king of Cyprus who fell in love with a statue of a woman he had made himself?
42. What was the name of the Roman god of sleep which is perpetuated in an English word meaning sleepy or drowsy?

Mythology : Other Myths and Legends

1. According to the legend, what creature did Saint George slay?
2. What is the name of the famous castle in Cornwall where King Arthur is supposed to have been born?

3. Which mythological British king was renowned for his love of music, food and tobacco?
4. According to the legend, where did Robin Hood and his merry men live?
5. What mythological creature was half eagle – half lion?
6. The Egyptian God Anubis had the body of a man and the head of which animal?
7. In folklore, what name is given to the sea-creature which has the body of a woman and the tail of a fish?
8. What is the name of the legendary spectral ship which is believed to haunt the Cape of Good Hope?
9. In Robert Burns' poem *Tam O'Shanter* the hero used a legendary method of escaping from witches. What was it?
10. With which legendary heroine is the City of Coventry associated?
11. Who was the King of Phrygia who was given the questionable gift of turning everything he touched into gold?
12. Who was the ancient Eygptian God of the sun?
13. Frey was the God of Fertility and Freya was the Goddess of Love, according to which mythology?
14. In Arthurian legend, what was the 'Holy Grail' for which King Arthur's knights searched?
15. Who, with the aid of his mighty sword called Hrunting, was responsible for the deaths of the feared monster Grendel and Grendel's mother?
16. What do you acquire if you kiss the Blarney Stone?
17. What was the name of the mythical English woman who was supposed to have become Pope in 855 as John VIII?
18. The Lorelei is the name of a rocky cliff on a European river with a remarkable echo – the legendary home of a maiden whose song lured boatmen to destruction. On which river is the Lorelei located?
19. What kind of creature was a silkie?
20. Who, according to legend, was King Arthur's treacherous son?

21. When Lady Godiva rode through the streets of Coventry, who, according to legend, was struck blind?

22. What name is given in Scandinavian mythology to describe the special paradise to which the souls of warriors slain in battle were transported?

23. What was the name of the minstrel in Robin Hood's company? (Robin helped to carry off the minstrel's bride when she was about to be married to an old knight against her will.)

24. Legend has it that a Japanese girl was told that her future husband would live as many years as a flower has petals, so she divided each petal of a carnation into sections and created a new flower. What flower?

25. According to legend, how many knights sat at the Round Table of King Arthur?

26. Who were Gog and Magog?

27. What was the name of Dick Turpin's mare?

28. What name is given to the tortoise at the South Pole on which the earth is said to rest?

Names : People

1. Who was the fourth Earl of Sandwich who, according to legend, gave his name to this snack?

2. What was Calamity Jane's married name?

3. John Bull is the imaginary figure who represents Great Britain. What is the name of his American counterpart?

4. Who was known as Lord Greystoke?

5. What name is given to a native or inhabitant of Oxford?

6. Who were known as the conquistadores?

7. By what name are the Society of Friends better known?
8. In which city in Great Britain are the inhabitants called Novacastrians?
9. Who was known as The British Cicero?
10. What name was used to describe a Roman officer who had command of a hundred men?
11. By what name are the aboriginal population of New Zealand known?
12. In the Netherlands and Belgium on December 6th Sinter Klaas brings gifts to children according to tradition. What is the name of Sinter Klaas' assistant?
13. What was the maiden name of Shakespeare's mother?
14. The pupils of which school are sometimes referred to as Salopians?
15. Which French writer gave his name to a form of sexual perversion that delights in the infliction of cruelty?

Names : Places, Things & Events

1. What name is given to the time of the year when the sun appears directly overhead at the Equator at noon?
2. What is another name for kaolin?
3. What is the poetic name for Ireland?
4. What is the name of the world news agency based in London which is named after its founder-owner?
5. Why is damask linen so named?
6. What is the name of the US Military Academy which is north of New York City?
7. What name was given to the first all-British artificial satellite?

8. Name the refreshing perfume whose invention is attributed to Giovanni Maria Farina, which takes its name from where it was manufactured.

9. Which famous London street is named after a street ball game – said to have originated in France?

10. The man-made material 'nylon' is much in use today. How did it come by its name?

11. What name is given to the hair of the Angora goat?

12. What name is given to the instrument used for measuring the distance covered by a pedestrian from the number of steps and their average length?

13. What parade celebrates the British sovereign's Birthday?

14. What name did *The Times* newspaper begin with in 1785, before changing to its present title in 1788?

15. What name was given to the list of publications that the Roman Catholic Church forbade its members to read except by special permission?

16. What is the name of the Royal Military Academy in Berkshire?

17. What was the name of the German Parliament building which was set on fire in Berlin in February 1933 which marked a new stage in the Nazi reign of terror?

Names : Shared Names

1. A Scottish artist, a city of Michigan USA with large motor manufacturing plants and a compact, hard brittle rock all share which name?

2. Which planet and a kind of mollusc share the same name?

3. What name is shared by a very large bottle and an ancient Middle-Eastern King who captured Jerusalem in 598 BC and finally destroyed it?
4. The county town of the Isle of Wight, a resort and naval base on Rhode Island, and the county town of Gwent all share which name?
5. Which small falcon shares its name with a character from Arthurian legend?
6. An invention patented by R W Thompson (1845), the Scandinavian god of battles and a town in the Lebanon all share which name?
7. An English poet, a city of Kent and a port of New York all share which name?
8. Which fruit, river in South Africa, town in France and county metropolitan area of Southern California share the same name?
9. What name is shared by a miraculous Egyptian bird, the capital of Arizona and a group of Pacific islands?
10. Which town in Warwickshire shares its name with a public school and a type of football?

Nicknames

1. If Jack Tar is a British sailor, what name is given to a British soldier?
2. What was nicknamed Puffing Billy?
3. Which English football team is known by the nickname The Hammers?
4. Which American World Heavyweight boxing champion had the nickname The Brown Bomber?
5. Who was nicknamed The Beard by the US Intelligence Service?

6. Which inland country is sometimes referred to as the Roof of the World?

7. What is the common nickname given to the glass reflectors set into the middle of roads?

8. What is the nickname commonly given to the aircraft known as a Boeing 747?

9. Who, in the twentieth century, assumed the nickname Il Duce – a name meaning The Leader?

10. Which word is army slang for a recruit?

11. By what name is Nessiteras Rhombopteryx more familiarly known in Scotland?

12. Who was nicknamed Glorious John?

13. Name the entertainer known as the Tigress from Tiger Bay?

14. Who was known as Farmer George?

15. What was the nickname of Henry Percy, the eldest son of the first Earl of Northumberland?

16. Which Scottish town was nicknamed Auld Reekie?

17. Whose secret service code names are Potus and Flotus?

18. Who was nicknamed Impeesa, meaning The Wolf Who Never Sleeps, by the Matabele tribe?

19. What is the nickname given to the Stetson?

20. Who was known by the nickname The Forces' Sweetheart in World War II?

21. Which British newspaper gained the nickname The Thunderer?

22. Who was christened Supermac by the cartoonist Vicky in 1958?

23. Who was known as the Dancing Chancellor during Queen Elizabeth I's reign?

24. Who was known by the nickname The Little Corporal?

25. Who or what was given the nickname Big Bertha?

26. By what nickname were the British auxiliaries in Ireland, who tried to quell the rebellion of 1919–22, known?

27. Which historical figure was given the nicknames Old

Ironsides and Old Noll?

28. Which slang name may be applied to a magistrate or a master at a public school?

29. Give the name of the man described as 'the prisoner of Spandau'.

30. Which item of clothing was nicknamed 'inexpressibles'?

Numbers

1. How many pockets has a snooker table?

2. How many stars and stripes has the American flag?

3. How many psalms are there in The Book of Psalms?

4. In Casco Bay, Maine, USA, there are a number of islands whose name gives away their number. How many are there?

5. According to the narrative poem by Tennyson, how many horsemen took part in the Charge of the Light Brigade?

6. How many major trumps are there in a pack of tarot cards and how many cards in a tarot pack?

7. Which number is traditionally said to symbolise evil, because in Genesis it is only on this day that there is a failure to mention that God saw that his work was good?

8. How many days did the famous Long March of the Chinese Communists (1934–35) last?

9. How many lines has a limerick?

10. The 1926 version of the film *Don Juan* starring John Barrymore is reputed to be the film with the most kisses ever made. How many separate kisses are there in this film?

11. Approximately how many different ways are there in which the first eight moves of a game of chess can be played?

12. According to Genesis, the only woman whose life-span was recorded in the Bible is Sarah, a wife of Abraham. How old was she at her death?

13. What is the atomic number of gold?

14. How many books are there in the New Testament?

15. How old was Johann Wolfgang von Goethe when he finished his most famous work *Faust*?

16. How many coloured squares has a Rubik Cube?

17. According to the rhyme 'One is for Sorrow and Two is for Joy', what is seven for?

18. How many dalmatians are there in the children's book which was made into a film by Walt Disney?

19. What is the gestation period of a giraffe?

20. How many steps must you first climb if you wish to kiss the Blarney Stone (in Blarney Castle, County Cork, Eire)?

21. How many lines has a sonnet?

Nursery Rhymes

1. 'Ring-a-ring of roses, a pocket full of poses, Atishoo, atishoo, we all fall down.' What historical event does this favourite children's rhyme commemorate?

2. Exactly what did the Owl and the Pussycat take to sea with them in a beautiful pea-green boat?

3. Who had 10,000 men in the children's nursery rhyme?

4. Who 'kissed the girls and made them cry'?

5. What grows in 'Mary Mary quite contrary's garden'?

6. In the nursery rhyme, what description is given of Old King Cole?

7. In the children's nursery rhyme, where did Little Polly Flinders sit?

8. On which day was Solomon Grundy married?

9. How many wives had the man going to St Ives?

10. Who dug the grave for Cock Robin?

11. What was used to mend Jack's head after he had fallen down the hill?

12. In which rhyme do you meet the cow with the crumpled horn?

13. In the nursery rhyme, what did the little nut tree produce?

14. Lucy Locket lost her pocket. Who was the little girl who found it?

15. According to the nursery rhyme, what did the fine lady riding to Banbury Cross wear on her toes?

16. What was the only tune that Tom, the piper's son, could play?

17. What did the old lady who lived in a shoe feed her many children?

18. According to the nursery rhyme, what are little boys made of?

19. According to the children's nursery rhyme, who put pussy down the well?

20. What type of morning is mentioned in the rhyme *Here We Go Round the Mulberry Bush*?

21. When Humpty Dumpty fell off the wall who could not put him together again?

22. What did Wee Willie Winkie ask as he ran through the town?

23. According to the rhyme, where did the muffin man live?

24. For whom did Hickety Pickety, the black hen, lay her eggs?

25. What was Yankee Doodle's horse called?

26. When did the Queen of Hearts make some tarts?

27. Which three animals are mentioned in the rhyme *Hey Diddle, Diddle*?

28. What was the price of the pies in the *Simple Simon*

rhyme?

29. What was the name of the old lady who went to the cupboard to fetch her poor dog a bone?
30. Who was the boy mentioned in the rhyme, 'Oh dear, what can the matter be . . .'?
31. According to the rhyme, if Monday's child is fair of face, what is Wednesday's child?
32. According to the popular rhyme, what were the names of the 'two little dicky birds'?
33. In the rhyme *Rub-a-dub-dub*, what were the occupations of the three men in a tub?
34. What was the name of the little boy who sang for his supper in the popular nursery rhyme?
35. In the rhyme, one boy tried to drown pussy in the well. Who pulled pussy out?
36. In the nursery rhyme *Pease Porridge Hot*, how old was the porridge?
37. How many hairs did the barber need to make a wig after shaving the pig?
38. Where were the cows in the *Little Boy Blue* rhyme?
39. What did *The Little Crooked Man* buy with his crooked sixpence?
40. Who, according to the rhyme, 'caught fishes, in other men's ditches'?

Ornithology

1. Which is the largest British wild bird?
2. Which thrush is nicknamed the Storm Cock because it often sings before and during wild wet weather?
3. On what island was the Dodo discovered in the 17th century?
4. To what family of birds do the Blackbird and the

Robin belong?

5. The Erne is an alternative name for which bird?
6. Which bird, native to Great Britain, is nicknamed the Yaffle after its distinctive laughing cry?
7. Which bird is sometimes known as the Windhover?
8. What flightless bird was found in the British Isles until as late as 1840 but is now extinct?
9. By what name is the Mavis better known?
10. The Kookaburra bird of Australia has a nickname which it earned because of its peculiar call. What is the nickname?
11. The Shrike has derived a descriptive nickname from its habit of impaling insects, mice and nestlings on thorns. What is this other name?
12. The Capercaillie is a bird seen occasionally in the Highlands of Scotland. To what family of birds does it belong?
13. A South African predatory bird, known as the Secretary Bird, is notable for its skill in killing and eating what kind of creatures?
14. What kind of bird would be found in the following forms: Brent, Greylag, Bean and Barnacle?
15. Chinese fishermen devised an ingenious method of catching fish which consisted of training a bird to dive for fish and constricting its neck so that it could not swallow its catch. What kind of bird was used?

Places

1. Where in Great Britain would you find Beardown Man?
2. Which famous tourist attraction would you find at

Anaheim, California?

3. Where in the United Kingdom would you find a place called Twenty?

4. Which famous castle is the country seat of the Duke of Norfolk?

5. In which English county would you find the village of Borstal which gave its name to a system of dealing with young offenders?

6. Where in the United States of America is the nation's gold bullion depository?

7. Which British holiday resort is sometimes referred to as the Naples of the North?

8. What is the name of the artists' quarter in Paris?

9. Banbury Cross of the nursery rhyme is found in the market town of Banbury. Where in Britain would you find Banbury?

10. In which country is the European Court of Justice?

11. Where in the British Isles would you find Norris Castle, Godshill Model Village and Bembridge Windmill?

12. In the city of Venice, what links the Ducal Palace with the State Prison?

13. Where in Britain would you find the tombs of the Duke of Wellington and Lord Nelson?

14. Where is the only place in the United Kingdom where the mountain peaks are named after the men who climbed them?

15. What was the name of the site of the stone where Dick Whittington allegedly heard Bow Bells sound 'turn again'?

16. Give the name of the world's first Safari Park which opened in 1966.

17. Where in England is the famous birthplace and statue of King Alfred the Great?

18. What is the name of England's smallest city?

19. A cathedral in the county of Wiltshire has the tallest spire in England at approximately 404 feet high. Where is this cathedral?

20. Where would you find the world's largest movable flood barrier?
21. What is the biggest tourist attraction in Zambia?
22. Name the home of the 11th Duke of Marlborough and birthplace of Sir Winston Churchill.
23. In what place are to be found The Royal Gallery, St Stephen's Hall and the Central Lobby?
24. What name is given to the fashionable quarter in the west of London, which is vaguely defined as lying between Piccadilly and Oxford Street and includes Park Lane?
25. Which Australian city was named after Lady Caroline Lamb's statesman husband?
26. What is the name of the highest public house in Britain?
27. Which London park was the site of the Great Exhibition of 1851?
28. Pulteney Bridge in Bath was modelled on a bridge in Florence. What is the name of this Italian bridge?

Plants & Gardening

1. What is the popular name for the flowering house-plant *Impatiens walleriana*?
2. What would a gardener do with a dibber (or dibble)?
3. Charles Darwin described this carnivorous plant 'the most wonderful plant in the world'. It traps its victims between the halves of its leaves. What is the name of this plant?
4. What is the national flower of Mexico?
5. Which plant of the buttercup family is also known as Traveller's Joy and Old Man's Beard?

6. What is the name given to the female reproductive organ of a flower?

7. What term is used to describe a mature tree which has been closely pruned to produce a close rounded head of young branches?

8. Why is Reindeer Moss so called?

9. What is the popular name given to the Sea Aster or Starwort or *Aster tradescanti*?

10. What is the name of the three-leafed clover associated with St Patrick's Day?

11. Which tree or shrub of the willow family is cultivated especially for basket-making?

12. What is the collective name given to the black and green flies which gardeners find troublesome because they suck the sap of plants and disfigure their leaves?

13. In gardening, what name is given to the individual prong or tooth of a fork or rake?

14. What name describes a plant which is produced by crossing different varieties or species?

15. Which word describes a plant that can remain outdoors all year and can even withstand a degree of frost?

16. What is the popular name given to the wood hyacinth which is seen in English woods in April and May?

17. The African marigold and the French marigold are both actually natives of which country?

18. Which fruit's scientific name is *Prunus persica*?

19. What name is given to the craft and science of growing plants in liquid nutrients instead of soil?

20. Copra is used in the manufacture of margarine and candles. From what plant is copra obtained?

21. The Easter Lily is a beautiful houseplant with white trumpet-shaped flowers. Of which country is this Spring flower a native?

22. What name is given to the glass case for small plants which enjoy a humid atmosphere?

23. The Sun-dew and Bladderwort are the most common species of British plants with an unusual characteris-

tic. What is this unusual characteristic?

24. Which plant was featured on the reverse side of the three-pence piece which was minted between 1937 and 1967?

25. Which fruit did Columbus discover on the Guadeloupe Islands in 1493?

26. What is the world's tallest growing grass?

27. What is the name given to the field of knowledge concerned with the study of plants?

28. The branches of which tree, in mediaeval times, were most commonly used in the making of bows?

29. *Papaver rhoeas* is the most striking of Britain's cornfield weeds. By what name is it more commonly known?

30. What name is given to a plant's main root?

31. What is the popular name for the Royal Botanical Gardens, begun over 200 years ago, which house every type of plant?

32. What is the name of the fruit which is a cross between a raspberry and a blackberry?

33. To what family do the cabbage, cauliflower, Brussels sprout and kale vegetables belong?

34. What name is used to describe the controlled cutting back of a plant, usually a shrub or tree, with a particular end in view?

35. By what name is the flower truss of the hazel and willow trees known?

36. What name is generally given to the wild rose of the English countryside?

37. Which term describes a plant which is able to store water in its thick fleshy leaves or stems?

38. To which family of flowers does the Pimpernel belong?

39. What name is given to the green colouring matter found in most plants?

40. Cork is derived from the bark of a tree. From what kind of tree is it obtained?

41. What name is given to the fruit which is a cross

between a peach and a plum?

42. What flower is alternatively known as the Lent Lily?
43. Which shrub produces the flowers which are commonly known as May Blossom?
44. What name is given to the process by which water passes from the soil, into the roots of plants and up the stems?
45. The Carnation is the national flower of which country?
46. What is the name of the plant from which we get the fruit aubergine?
47. What name is commonly given to the seeds of the horse-chestnut tree?
48. What name is given to a joint in the stem of a plant from which leaves, buds or side shoots spring?
49. Which term describes a leaf with two or more colours?
50. Which orange-coloured dye is obtained from the flowers of the autumn crocus?

Politics : America

1. Who was President of the United States from 1963–69, holding office after John F Kennedy and before Richard M Nixon?
2. Who was the first American President to be assassinated?
3. The Wall Street crash in America happened in October 1929. Who was the President at the time?
4. Which US President's political philosophy was 'Speak softly and carry a big stick'?
5. Whom did George Bush defeat to gain the Presidency

of the United States of America in 1988?

6. Which former American President was originally known as Leslie Lynch King?

7. Richard M Nixon was President of the United States of America between 1969 and 1974. What does the 'M' in his name stand for?

8. What name was given to the principle of American policy which declined any European intervention in political affairs of the American continent?

9. Who was the American President who kept the US out of World War I until 1917, when they entered 'to make the world safe for democracy'?

10. Which American President was wounded in an assassination bid in 1981? Before surgery he said to surgeons, 'I hope you guys are Republicans'.

11. In which city in the USA was President Kennedy assassinated?

12. Who defeated Gerald Ford in the 1976 Presidential election and became the 39th President of the United States?

13. Which American President was paralysed in 1921 by polio, although he rarely allowed himself to be seen in a wheelchair?

14. What term was used to describe the wave of anti-Communist hysteria in America between 1947 and 1954, which resulted in the loss of careers and livelihoods of many innocent Americans?

15. Which animal is the emblem of the US Republican Party?

16. Who was the American politician who was elected Vice-President (1968) on a Republican ticket with Nixon, who resigned in 1973 after corruption charges were brought against him?

17. What was the name of the brief speech given by President Lincoln on 19 November 1863, which contained the famous statement of the principles of American government: 'of the people, by the people, for the people'?

18. In a message to Congress in 1941 Franklin D Roosevelt talked of the 'Four Freedoms'. What were these?

Politics : Britain

1. Who was the first man to become Prime Minister of Great Britain?
2. The Whigs is an old name for which political party?
3. The Prime Minister lives at No. 10 Downing Street, the Chancellor of the Exchequer lives at No. 11 – who lives at No. 12?
4. He was a British Socialist Politician who lived between 1897 and 1960 – best known as the architect of the National Health Service. Who was he?
5. Who was the first British Labour prime minister with a majority from his own party?
6. When was the seven hundredth anniversary of Parliament celebrated?
7. Which politician was chiefly responsible for the creation of the British Police force as we know it?
8. Britain joined the Common Market twelve years after the first application was made. In which year did Britain join?
9. Name the English Liberal politician who succeeded Clement Davies as Liberal leader in 1956.
10. Harold Wilson dropped the use of his first name and used 'Harold' (his middle name). Give his first name.
11. Which political term is used to describe the manipulation of voting districts to give an unfair advantage to one political party in an election?
12. Under whose leadership was the Parliamentary

Labour Party when it adopted the Red Rose as its symbol?

13. Who was the first Socialist MP (1892)?
14. The General Strike in 1926 was called in support of which Union?
15. Who headed the inquiry into the Brixton riots in 1981?
16. Which British politician popularised the maxim, 'One man's wage rise is another man's price increase'?
17. Name two of the four politicians who founded the Social Democratic Party in Great Britain and were nicknamed the Gang of Four?
18. Which English philanthropist led the Parliamentary campaign against the slave trade which was eventually abolished in Britain in 1807?
19. What colour are the seats in the House of Lords?
20. Who succeeded Harold MacMillan as the Prime Minister of Great Britain?
21. What other title is held by the First Lord of the Treasury?
22. Educated in early life at schools for the blind, he went through college to University. Elected MP for Sheffield Brightside in 1987, he was created an Opposition Front Bench Spokesman in 1988. Can you name him?
23. The Government of the United Kingdom is shared by the three Estates. The House of Commons and the House of Lords are two. What is the third?
24. Who was the first Labour Prime Minister to form a government, in 1924?
25. The Speaker presides over debates in the House of Commons. What is his opposite number in the House of Lords?
26. In World War I politics who was known as the 'Welsh Wizard'?

Politics : Rest Of The World

1. What is the Icelandic Parliament called?
2. For how many years is a French President elected?
3. Who was the leader of Zanu who became Zimbabwe's first president?
4. Which Soviet leader did Leonid Brezhnev and Alexei Kosygin replace in a Kremlin coup in October 1964?
5. In which self-governing country did women first obtain the right to vote in a national election?
6. Who was the Chilean political leader who overthrew the Marxist Allende regime in 1973 and took control of the government?
7. In which year were South African sportsmen and women re-admitted to international team competitions after the dismantling of Apartheid?
8. Who was the German diplomat and statesman who was chief architect of the German Empire?
9. In which country is the Cortes the Parliament?
10. What are the two main political parties in the Republic of Ireland called?
11. Who led the Polish Solidarity Trade Union which confronted the Communist government in 1980?
12. Who was Hitler's propaganda minister during the 1933–1945 period?
13. In which country is the Parliament known as the Knesset?
14. He was a 16th Century Italian statesman who gave his name to a word meaning unscrupulous political cunning. Who was he?
15. What was the name of the town in South Africa which

was the scene of civil disturbances in 1960 after police fired into the black African crowd demonstrating against the Pass Laws?

16. Who was the church leader who became President of Cyprus in 1960?

17. What name was given to the cultural and political movement which sought to re-establish a Jewish national state in Palestine?

18. Who was the Boer who fought against the British in the Boer War and later became twice Prime Minister of South Africa, in 1919 and 1939?

19. Name the Israeli political leader who was awarded the Nobel Peace Prize in 1978.

20. What is the name of the National Parliament of the Irish Republic?

21. Which country became a Republic on January 26th 1950 but chose to remain within the Commonwealth?

22. What is the name of the inlet in southern Cuba which was the scene of the attempt in 1961 to overthrow the Communist regime of Fidel Castro?

Quotes

1. Which American President in 1856 observed: 'The ballot is stronger than the bullet'?

2. Complete the famous war-time speech by Sir Winston Churchill: 'Let us therefore brace ourselves to our duties and so bear ourselves that if the British Empire and its Commonwealth last for a thousand years, men will still say . . .'?

3. Who said, 'I couldn't help it – I can resist everything

except temptation'?

4. Who was it that complained of Prime Minister Gladstone in the following terms: 'He speaks to me as if I was a public meeting'?

5. Who was the Merry Monarch whose dying words were: 'Let not poor Nellie starve'?

6. Whose final words were: 'So little done, so much to do'?

7. Which American financier is said to have commented, 'Money is like manure. You have to spread it around or it smells'?

8. In 1989 who proclaimed that 'the Communist Party has no God-given right to rule'?

9. Who is attributed to have said, 'An army marches on its stomach'?

10. Who, upon seeing all her children at her bedside in 1964, said, 'Am I dying, or is this my birthday'?

11. Which composer is credited with the quotation, 'I shall hear in heaven'?

12. Which British playwright said, 'Never trust a man with short legs – brains too near their bottoms'?

13. Which millionaire philanthropist, born in Dunfermline in Scotland, before making his fortune in the USA, once said, 'The man who dies rich – dies disgraced'?

14. To whom is attributed the following famous words: 'Let them eat cake'?

15. Which American radical's slogan of 1968 was 'You're either part of the solution of part of the problem'?

16. Which American author is accredited with the famous words, 'If in doubt, tell the truth'?

17. Which British writer, in *How To Become A Virgin* (1981), said, 'Never keep up with the Joneses. Drag them down to your level. It's cheaper'?

18. Which politician, when defending her policies in 1980, said, 'The lady's not for turning'?

19. Which British fashion designer said, 'A woman is as young as her knee'?

20. In his first address to the American Congress in 1941, who said, 'If my father had been American and my mother British, instead of the other way round, I might have got here on my own'?

21. Which King who died in 1625 said, 'Smoking is a custom loathsome to the eye, hateful to the nose, harmful to the brain, dangerous to the lungs'?

22. Who said in 1969, 'That's one small step for man, one giant leap for mankind'?

23. Which American president's last words in 1945 were: 'I have a terrific headache'?

24. Which Swedish film star, on refusing to perform ever again in the mid-Fifties, said, 'I have made enough faces'?

25. Who said, in a speech in Washington in 1963, 'I have a dream that one day this nation will rise up, live out the true meaning of its creed – we hold these truths as self-evident, that all men are created equal'?

26. Who, in 1936, said, 'Dickie, this is absolutely terrible . . . I am quite unprepared for it . . . I've never even seen a state paper. I'm only a Naval officer, it's the only thing I know about'?

27. 'Guns will make us powerful – butter will only make us fat'. This statement was broadcast by a Nazi in 1936 who committed suicide ten years later. Who was he?

28. Which American President in his inaugural speech said, 'Let us never negotiate out of fear, but let us never fear to negotiate'?

29. Which Russian said, 'It is true that liberty is precious – so precious that it must be rationed'?

30. Who wrote: 'Had we lived, I would have had a tale to tell of the hardihood, endurance and courage of my companions which would have stirred the hearts of Englishmen'?

31. Which French cosmetician said, 'There are no ugly women, only lazy ones'?

32. Which MP was jeered on his first speech in Parliament and on sitting down said, 'Though I sit down

now, the time will come when you will hear me'?

33. Who said, 'In war, whichever side may call itself the victor, there are no winners, but all are losers'?

34. Who, on the eve of his country's independence, said, 'We made a tryst with destiny . . . At the stroke of the midnight hour when the world sleeps, India will awake to life and freedom'?

Ranks & Titles

1. When a man is given a knighthood he takes on the title Sir. What title does his wife take?

2. What was the title given to the eldest son of the King of France?

3. What is the hereditary title held by the spiritual head of the Ismaeli sect of Moslems who claim descent from Fatima, daughter of the prophet Mohammed?

4. In Japan, under the old feudal system, what title was given to members of the military class noted for their sword-play?

5. What are the relative ranks in the Army and Royal Air Force to that of an Admiral in the Royal Navy?

6. What is the correct title given to the daughter of an Earl, Marquis, or Duke?

7. What police rank is immediately senior to chief inspector?

8. In the British peerage, what is the third title in order of rank coming between Marquess and Viscount?

9. Which monarch had as one of his titles 'The Lion of Judah'?

10. What title is given in Spain to daughters of the sovereign?

11. What title was awarded to Sir Arthur Wellesley in 1814 following his brilliant leadership in the Napoleonic Wars?
12. What title is given to an English judge who presides over the Court of Appeal and ranks immediately below the Lord Chief Justice?
13. If a nobleman from a European country held the title of Count, what is the equivalent title in Britain?
14. Lieutenant Commander in the Navy and Squadron Leader in the Air Force are equivalent in rank. What is the equivalent in rank to both in the Army?

Religion : Christian

1. Which Christian festival is commemorated on Easter Day?
2. Which sisterhood established at Assisi around 1212 adopted the Franciscan rule and habit?
3. What is the name of the churchbell rung in Roman Catholic countries at morning, noon and sunset?
4. Which Christian movement was established by George Williams in England in 1844?
5. What is the first day of Holy Week known as?
6. John Wesley – the founder of the Methodist Church – had a brother who became equally famous for writing many fine hymns. What was his brother's Christian name?
7. What title is given to the president of the General Assembly of the Church of Scotland?
8. What name is given to the formalised religious painting, popular with the Eastern Church, which is

generally painted on a wooden panel?

9. What does Maundy Thursday commemorate – falling as it does on the day before Good Friday?

10. Which organisation, belonging to the Church of England, was founded by Wilson Carlile in 1882?

11. In which country of the world would you find adherents of the Coptic Church?

12. *The Watch Tower* is a magazine associated with which religious group?

13. Which custom was officially abolished by the Vatican Council in the mid-sixties, though it continues to be practised in some Catholic countries?

14. Which order of friars are called the White Friars, because of their white habits?

15. William Booth founded the Salvation Army – prior to this he was a minister in which religion?

16. Who founded the Church of England?

17. Who was the leader of the Mormons who led his people across the American Mid-West to found Salt Lake City?

18. On the cross on which Jesus was crucified were the initials INRI. What does this mean?

19. In the Latin Church, what is the name given to the candle which is lit on Easter Eve to represent the new light of Christ, 'the light of the world'?

20. Which religious sect was founded by J N Darby and E Cronin?

21. What is the name of the Christian Sacrament in which bread and wine are consecrated and received as the body and blood of Jesus?

22. Where was it that Christians first gave eggs to their friends at Easter to remind them of the resurrection of Jesus?

23. By what name is the Collegiate Church of St Peter in London better known?

24. Who distributed the first Bibles to hotels in the year 1908?

25. In the Western Church what are the Ember Days?

26. Which American founded the religious movement The Jehovah's Witnesses, the followers of whom believe that Christ returned invisibly in 1874 and that Armageddon is near?
27. What were the names of the followers of Ignatius Loyola?
28. What is the name of the first day in Lent?
29. What is the name of the Christian movement started by F William Miller in 1863 which looks in anticipation to the return of Christ in Person?
30. Mary Baker Eddy, an American woman, founded and developed a religion which denied not only the reality of pain but also the existence of the grave. What was the religion called?
31. What are encyclical letters?
32. What is the name of the most austere order of monks of the Roman Catholic Church who live in individual cells and rarely meet others unless in public worship?
33. What name is given to the statement of principal Christian beliefs?
34. For which day are Hot Cross Buns traditionally reserved?
35. What is the name of the Vatican's Army?
36. What name is given to the feast of the Blessed Sacrament observed on the Thursday after Trinity Sunday?

Religion : Non-Christian

1. Which of the world's religions teaches an Eightfold Path to destroy suffering?
2. Under Islamic law, how many wives is a man allowed to have at one time?

3. In which religion do Vishnu and Shiva play a major role and what are they?
4. In which religion are the Shabuoth or the Festival of Weeks and Succoth celebrated?
5. What are the three colours of the Rastafarian religion?
6. By what name is the ancient religion of Japan known?
7. What is the name of the Hindu custom involving the voluntary cremation of a widow on her husband's funeral pyre?
8. Which religious group began as followers of a pious young man called Nanak (1469–1538)?
9. What were the Celtic class of priests known as?
10. In Muslim countries, what is the custom known as purdah?
11. Who is the spiritual head of the Yellow Hat sect of the Buddhist religion of Tibet?
12. Moslems are the adherents of what religion?
13. What are the two symbols of Judaism?
14. The Caaba is a sacred building containing a black stone said to have fallen from Paradise with Adam and given by Gabriel to Abraham. Where is the Caaba?
15. In 1967 this European Communist country became the only state in the world to ban all organised religion. Name it.
16. The golden Dome of the Rock is one of the most sacred shrines of which religion?
17. Divali, or the Festival of Lights, is an important celebration in which religion?
18. What term is used to mean 'fit to be eaten according to Jewish ritual'?
19. Which religious sect regard the late Haile Selassie I, former Emperor of Ethiopia, as divine, the king of kings and lord of lords?
20. What is the name of the forbidden river beyond which no pure Hindu can pass?
21. Most Sikhs wear the five Ks: Kes, Kangha, Kirpan,

Kara and Kaccha. What are they?

22. What is the book of the Islamic religion called?
23. Can you name the most sacred of all the holy places of the Jewish religion?
24. An Arabic word, meaning poor, was given to a Hindu or Moslem holy man who led an ascetic life. What was the word?
25. Which religious group come from all over the world to pray at Bodhgaya?
26. What name is given to the Festival of the Jewish New Year?
27. What name is given to the ninth month of the Muslim year, when daily fasting is observed between sunrise and sunset?
28. What name is given to the four holy books of the Hindus?
29. Of which religion are the eight-spoked wheel and the lotus flower symbols?
30. What is the name given to the encyclopedia of Jewish laws and traditions which supplement the first five books of the Old Testament?

Royalty

1. Queen Victoria was Britain's longest reigning monarch; she lived four days longer than Britain's longest reigning King. Who was he?
2. What name is given to the money voted annually by Parliament to pay for the personal expenses of the sovereign?
3. Which is the only case in British history of a husband and wife ruling jointly as King and Queen?

4. Which momentous occasion took place on June 2nd, 1953?
5. What caused Prince Albert's death in 1861?
6. What was the official residence of British Sovereigns between 1698 and 1837?
7. What are the three other Christian names of Prince Charles?
8. Which King was the first member of the British Royal Family to own and drive a motor car?
9. What was the official name of the British royal family prior to 1917 when the House of Windsor was adopted?
10. What is the name of the grand castle in Scotland where Princess Margaret was born in 1930?
11. In 1936 King Edward VIII abdicated from the British throne to marry an American divorcee. Who was she?
12. What is the name of the ancestral home of the Dukes of Bedford?
13. Who was the only one of Queen Elizabeth II's children to be born at Clarence House?
14. Which estate, a popular retreat of the Royal Family, was bought by Prince Albert for £31,000?
15. Which French King was distinguished by the fact that he had two teeth when he was born?
16. One of the titles of British monarchs is 'Fidei Defensor'. What does this mean?
17. Who married Lady Elizabeth Bowes-Lyon?
18. At 13 years of age Prince Charles followed in his father's footsteps by attending the same school. Name the school.
19. Who was the last English King to die in battle?
20. Where was Queen Elizabeth II when she delivered her first Christmas message?
21. Why did Prince Michael of Kent have to renounce his right to the succession to the English throne?
22. What name is given to the royal family of the Netherlands?
23. Which royal wrote *Competition Carriage Driving*?

24. In 1953 the Queen's yacht *Britannia* replaced the fifty year old yacht of Queen Victoria's. What was the name of this yacht?
25. In which year was Prince Charles crowned Prince of Wales at Caernarvon Castle?
26. What relation, prior to marriage, was Prince Albert to Queen Victoria?
27. Who was known as Madame Deficit?
28. In what year was Prince Henry (Harry) born?
29. Who represented the Queen at the state funeral of Princess Grace of Monaco in 1982?
30. Who was Queen of England for only nine days?
31. By what name was King Edward VIII known after his abdication in 1936?
32. Which title, which was created by Edward I of England in 1301, is conferred on the eldest son of the monarch?
33. In 1745 she married Peter III, whom she later deposed and murdered. Who was she?
34. Which King was known as 'the turnip hoer'?
35. Which member of the British Royal Family wrote the children's story, *The Old Man of Lochnagar*?
36. What is the name of the Queen's country home in Norfolk?

Saints

1. Nossa Senhora da Aparecida is the patron saint of which country?
2. Which saint's day falls on the 30th of November?
3. Who is the patron saint of toothache?
4. Which saint is known as the Boy Bishop?

5. When is St Sylvester's night?
6. Which French saint, who advocated the Little Way of Goodness in the small things in everyday life, is known as the Little Flower of Jesus?
7. Which saint's day falls on April 23rd?
8. Whose shrine was brought to Durham in 995, after being removed from Holy Island to escape Viking raids?
9. Who was regarded as the patron saint of drinking and jovial meetings as well as of reformed drunkards?
10. Name the Irish monk who founded the monastery on the island of Lindisfarne.
11. Which saint was murdered at Canterbury Cathedral in 1170 AD?
12. Who is the patron saint of shoe-makers whose feast day is celebrated on 25th October?
13. What is traditionally considered to be the burial site of St Peter, leader of the Twelve Disciples?
14. Which Italian friar was originally known as Giovanni di Bernardone?
15. Which saint was born at Lourdes?
16. Who is the patron saint of wine growers?
17. Who is the patron saint of tax collectors?
18. Which Basque Jesuit missionary was known as the Apostle to the Indies?
19. To which saint is the first day after Christmas dedicated?
20. Who is the patron saint of grave diggers?
21. Who is the patron saint of France and was the first bishop of Paris who built a church on an island in the Seine?
22. Who is the patron saint of dancers and comedians?
23. Sometimes known as St Kentigern, he is the patron saint of Glasgow and is buried in Glasgow Cathedral. He died in AD 603. By what name is he more familiarly known?
24. Who is the patron saint of music?

Science : Common Names

1. By which initials do we more commonly know Dichlorodiphenyltrichloroethane?
2. By what name is solid carbon dioxide known?
3. What is another name for vitamin B_2?
4. Deoxyribonucleic acid is more commonly known by which initials?
5. By what name is nitrous oxide more commonly known?
6. What name did mediaeval alchemists give to the imaginary substance which it was believed could turn base metals into gold?
7. By what initials is trichlorophenylmethyliodosalicyl better known?
8. What is the meaning of the abbreviation UHF?
9. It was formerly known as brimstone – what is it now called?
10. By which initials is trinitrotoluene better known?
11. By what name is hydrated magnesium sulphate more commonly known?
12. What is the name of the white crystalline alkaloid derived from opium?
13. What is the name given to the explosive which consists of nitroglycerine, nitrocellulose, wood pulp and potassium nitrate?
14. What name is given to the green or greenish-blue deposit which forms on copper or brass, like rust?
15. What is the common name for sodium chloride?
16. What chemical element is the common constituent of diamonds, soot and coal?

17. By what name is the white crystalline powder diamorphine hydrochloride more commonly known?
18. It is sometimes called oil of vitriol. What is it otherwise known as?
19. In modern technological terms, what does LPG stand for?
20. The word 'laser' is made up from the initial letters of its meaning. What do the letters represent?

Science :
Solids, Liquids & Gases

1. What is the lightest known substance?
2. Name the substance or solution which is generally used to preserve biological specimens. It can also be used as a disinfectant and in the manufacture of some plastics.
3. What name is given to an alloy of mercury?
4. What is the name of the acid found in oranges, limes and lemons?
5. What name is given to the instrument used to measure gas pressure?
6. How many carats has pure gold?
7. Which word describes the property of a metal which allows it to be drawn out into wire?
8. What is the name of the colourless, odourless, inert gas isolated by Daniel Rutherford in 1772 and known by the chemical symbol N?
9. From what raw material is aluminium obtained?
10. Bell metal is an alloy of which two metals?
11. Name two of the three main constituents of glass.

12. Which gas is sometimes referred to as Marsh Gas?
13. What is the name of the copper and zinc alloy used in imitation of gold?
14. Which is the only common metal which is liquid at room temperature?
15. What name is given to the art of working metals?
16. What is the chief metal which is alloyed with iron to make stainless steel?
17. What metal, when in ribbon or powder form, burns with a brilliant white light?
18. What is the name of the acid in vinegar and spoiled wine?
19. What is the name of the process whereby iron or steel sheets are plated with zinc, to protect them from corrosion from the atmosphere?
20. What is the inert gas used in balloons and airships, because of its lightness and non-inflammability?
21. What metal is a main constituent of both brass and bronze?
22. What kind of acid is normally used in a car battery?

Science : Studies & Theories

1. What is the name of the branch of physics which deals with the propagation and detection of sound?
2. What name is given to the study of the paths taken by projectiles, for example, bullets or rockets?
3. In which field of science did Michael Faraday carry out experiments and make exciting discoveries?
4. Which scientific principle states that when a body is immersed in water, the apparent loss in weight is equal to the weight of the water displaced?

5. What name is given to the science that studies the flow of fluids?
6. What theory is commenced with the formula $E = mc^2$?
7. What is the name of the science which deals with drugs and their effect on man and animals?
8. What name is given to the study of water upon, under and above the earth's surface?
9. What is the name given to the biological science concerning heredity?
10. What name is given to the study of earthquakes and tremors?
11. With what is the science of ergonomics concerned?
12. British scientist Lord Ernest Rutherford won a Nobel Prize in 1908. In which field of science did he work?
13. With what is the science of cryogenics concerned?
14. Who developed the theory of relativity?

Science : Symbols & Numbers

1. Which metal has the chemical symbol Ag?
2. What is the chemical symbol for mercury?
3. Which soft corrosion-resistant metal is known by the chemical symbol Pt?
4. What element has the atomic number 1?
5. What is the chemical symbol for tin?
6. What is the chemical symbol for lead?
7. Wolfram – with the chemical symbol W – is used for hardening steel. By what name is it now known?
8. What chemical element is represented by the symbol Cu?
9. What is the chemical symbol for sodium?

10. What element has the atomic number 82?
11. What is the chemical symbol for gold?
12. What is the chemical symbol for chlorine?
13. What is the atomic number of plutonium?
14. Name the element you would identify by the symbol K.

Science : Terms & Equipment

1. What is the name of the process whereby plants make food for themselves?
2. What term is used to describe lines drawn on charts linking together points of equal barometric pressure?
3. In acoustics, what name is given to the numerical expression of relative loudness of a sound?
4. What would be measured with an anemometer?
5. In dyeing, what name is given to the substance used for fixing colouring matter?
6. In biology, what is the name of the clear fluid which forms 55% of blood?
7. What is the name of the main protein of milk?
8. What name is given to the lowest temperature theoretically possible?
9. What is the general term for minute organisms found drifting near the surface of seas or lakes?
10. What is the name of the fine white powder produced by heating gypsum, used for casts and moulds?
11. On what are earthquakes measured?
12. What is the name of the instrument used for measuring atmospheric pressure?
13. What name is given to the visible electric discharge seen at wingtips of aircraft caused by static electricity

in the atmosphere?

14. What name is given to any substance which speeds up or slows down the rate of chemical reaction, but is itself unchanged at the end of the reaction?

15. What is the name of the instrument used for measuring the current flowing in an electric circuit?

16. On which temperature scale is the boiling point of water 212°?

17. What is the unit used to measure speed above the speed of sound (i.e. supersonic speed)?

18. There are three forms of heat transference: convection and conduction are two. What is the third?

19. What is the name of the instrument used for measuring the amount of water vapour in the atmosphere?

20. What term is used to describe lines drawn on charts through points of equal temperature?

21. What is the name of the sugar found in milk?

22. What is the name of the instrument used for detecting and measuring radioactivity?

23. In meteorological terms, the Beaufort scale – from 0-12 – describes wind force. Force 10 is described as a whole gale. Force 12 is a hurricane. What descriptive term is applied to Force 11 on the Beaufort Scale?

24. What name was given to the extremely accurate clock which was invented so that navigators could find their longitude?

Ships & The Sea

1. Lord Nelson's famous flagship is moored at Portsmouth. What is the name of this ship?

2. Name the top four ranks in the Royal Navy.

3. Which nautical term is used to describe those areas of

the Atlantic and Pacific Oceans where the weather is usually dead calm, hot and sultry but liable to change suddenly to squall?

4. Which German Battleship was outmanoeuvred by three British Cruisers and finally scuttled in the River Plate in 1939?

5. At sea, time is marked in bells. How many bells are there at the end of a watch?

6. What was the name of the craft in which Sir Francis Chichester circumnavigated the world?

7. What was the name of Captain Cook's ship in which he sailed on his first voyage of discovery in 1768?

8. The passenger liner *Queen Elizabeth* came to a tragic end in 1972. How and where?

9. What flag is flown by a vessel about to leave port?

10. What was the name of the world's first large propeller-driven steamship and where would you find this ship today?

11. What kind of vessel was the *Cutty Sark*?

12. What is the name of the warship which sank on its maiden voyage in 1628 and is now restored in Stockholm?

13. How many feet are there in a nautical fathom?

14. What was the name of the sailing ship found mysteriously deserted and drifting in the North Atlantic near the Azores on 7th November 1872?

15. The port side of a ship is the left-hand side. By what name was it known before the Admiralty changed the name to port in 1844?

16. What was the name of the ship in which the Pilgrim Fathers set sail in 1620 bound for the American continent?

17. In 1970 Thor Heyerdahl crossed the Atlantic in a most unusual craft. What was its name and what was it made of?

18. What award is held by the ship which makes the fastest crossing of the Atlantic Ocean?

19. Which English king is given credit for founding the

Royal Navy?

20. In which ship did Captain Scott sail on his voyage and expedition to the Antarctic?

21. With which building do you associate all matters concerning navigation?

22. What was a U Boat?

23. The Duke of Medina Sidonia in 1588 led an ambitious enterprise. Of what was he in command?

24. What colour of Ensign does the Merchant Navy fly?

25. He was a famous sailor – born in Plymouth – who, in 1789, was cast adrift from the ship *Bounty* by his mutinous crew. Who was he?

26. Who founded the Royal National Lifeboat Institution in 1824?

27. The sound of the Lutine Bell is dreaded in the maritime world. Why?

28. For which race was the America's Cup originally offered by the Royal Yacht Squadron in 1851?

29. In what year did Francis Drake begin his voyage around the world?

30. Nelson defeated the French Navy in the Battle of the Nile, but which navy did he destroy at the Battle of Copenhagen in 1801?

31. In which shipyards were the *Queen Mary* and *QE2* built?

32. In the International Code used by shipping, what is the meaning of the signal RY flying from the masthead?

33. What was the name of the world's first atomic-powered merchant ship of 1959?

34. What are the three main types of docks?

35. What was the *Kon-Tiki*?

36. What was the name of the first vessel in the world to be driven by nuclear power?

37. What were the *Clermont* and the *Comet*?

38. What name is given to the small Welsh boats used by fishermen which are made of canvas stretched over a wicker frame?

Sport : Athletics & Gymnastics

1. Who was the athlete who, in the space of 40 days in 1979, broke the world records for the 800 metres, 1500 metres and the mile?
2. What is the essential difference between the modern pentathlon and the decathlon?
3. In what athletic event do the winners only move backwards?
4. Approximately what length is the fibreglass pole used in the pole vault?
5. The triple jump is a standard field event for men on the programme of all major athletics championships. By what other name is it known?
6. In men's gymnastics, name the six pieces of apparatus on which they perform.
7. Who was the American long-jumper who put himself into the history books with one leap – a monstrous 8.90 metres – which won him the 1968 Olympic title, beating the previous world record by 54.6 cm?
8. Which athletic events all take place from circles?
9. Who was the first runner to break the four-minute-mile barrier?
10. In gymnastics, what name is given to the last movement of an exercise when the gymnast descends from the apparatus?
11. A Finnish athlete achieved a double Olympic gold in 1972 and repeated the feat in 1976 by winning the 5,000 and 10,000 metre races on both occasions. Who was he?
12. Which Scottish athlete, running her first-ever

marathon, won the 1991 New York marathon?

13. She was born on 12th December 1961 and was discovered as a gymnast at the age of seven. In the 1976 Montreal Olympics she made history with six perfect scores of ten. Give her name.

14. Which group of British athletics meetings is believed to have originated from the action of a local ruler, dissatisfied with the speed of his messengers, who held races among his retainers to the top of the nearest hill and back, rewarding the first man home with a purse of gold and the second with a sword?

15. Name the athlete who won four gold medals in the 1936 Berlin Olympic Games.

Sport : Cricket

1. How long is a cricket pitch, from stump to stump?
2. Who was the first Australian cricketer to be knighted?
3. When did cricket start in Great Britain?
4. In cricket, 111 is believed to be an unlucky score. What is the name given to this score?
5. In cricket fielding positions, where does first slip stand?
6. Which county cricket club plays its home matches at Edgbaston?
7. What is a 'peg' in cricket?
8. Who was the first cricketer to score a maximum six sixes in one over?
9. How many players are there in a cricket team?
10. W G Grace became a legendary Gloucestershire cricketer. What did his initials represent?
11. What name is given to a ball delivered by the bowler

so that it pitches directly under the bat?

12. Which cricket club, established in 1787, eventually became the game's ruling authority?

13. In the game of cricket, what is meant by the phrase 'a pair of spectacles'?

14. Which county cricket club plays home matches at The Oval?

15. What name is given to the cricketers' year book, where all the cricketing laws and scores are reported?

16. Which early nineteenth century bowler was known as the Nonpareil?

17. In cricket, what word is used to describe an off-break, bowled to a right-handed batsman with what appears to be a leg-break action?

Sport : Football

1. In what year was the first FA Cup Final held at Wembley?

2. Which football club's ground was used as a prisoner of war camp until May 1945 during the Second World War?

3. Which football league club plays its home matches at Old Trafford?

4. Which English football team is known as The Saints?

5. By what name was the UEFA Cup known prior to the 1971–72 season?

6. In what year was the first official international between Scotland and England in football?

7. Which football club, founded in 1880, was also known as The Old Invincibles and The Lillywhites?

8. In which year was the first Wembley FA final to

require a replay?

9. Which football league club plays its home matches at Highbury?
10. Which English football team is known as The Rams?
11. Wembley Stadium was opened in 1923 in time for the FA Cup Final. Can you name the two teams who played this final?
12. Which English footballer was known as the 'wizard of dribble'?
13. In what year was FIFA (International Federation of Football Associations) formed?
14. Who captained the English World Cup winning soccer team at Wembley in 1966 when England beat West Germany by four goals to two?
15. What is the name of Leeds United's home ground?
16. Which Scottish football team plays its home games at Hampden Park?
17. Name one of the national teams to compete in the first World Cup football competition final in 1930.
18. Which Scottish football club plays its home games on a ground called Tynecastle?
19. Name the manager who took the Republic of Ireland football team to the 1994 World Cup Finals.
20. Which famous English football club plays its home games at Anfield?

Sport : Golf

1. How many holes are there on a golf course?
2. Which golfer had a massive band of followers collectively known as Arnie's Army?
3. What is the maximum number of golf clubs a golfer is

allowed to use in a game?

4. What is the name of the links of The Honourable Company of Edinburgh Golfers founded in 1744?
5. In golf, what is a foursome?
6. On which Scottish golf course is the eighth hole popularly known as The Postage Stamp (the shortest hole in championship golf at 125 yds)?
7. Which golfer captured the headlines in 1970, when he became the first British golfer for half a century to win the US Open?
8. In golf, what phrase is used to describe an area of particularly dense rough on the course?
9. Who was the only golfer ever to win the British Open, British Amateur, American Open and American Amateur titles in the same year, achieving the remarkable feat in 1930?
10. In golf, what is the traditional name for the number 3 wood?
11. What is a double bogey?
12. The earliest reference to the sport of golf is in a Scottish Parliamentary law of 1457 forbidding the game of golf to be played because it interfered with the practice of what other activity?
13. In golf, what is the traditional name for the number 10 iron?
14. In 1987 Britain managed a double that it had never done before, winning both the US Women's Open and the Open Championship. Can you name both the golfers who achieved this for their countries with just a week between the winning of each title?
15. In golfing parlance, what is an eagle?
16. In golf, what is the meaning of a birdie?

Sport : Horses

1. Where is the classic horse race the St Leger run?
2. Why can the same horse not win the English Derby in successive years?
3. Where are the headquarters of the Jockey Club?
4. What is the name of the vehicle in which the driver sits in harness racing?
5. On which race course is the 1000 Guineas run?
6. On which race course is the King George VI Chase run?
7. What is the name of the magnificent race course near Paris which is virtually the headquarters of the turf in France?
8. Where is the All England Jumping Course?
9. What is the name of the Argentinian sport for horsemen which is a cross between polo and netball and requires the skills of a circus rider?
10. Name the four types of horse racing.
11. Which famous race meeting was instituted by Queen Anne in 1711?
12. What is the name of the classic horse race, founded in 1809, competed for over the straight Rowley Mile course at Newmarket?
13. Which three horse races make up the American Triple Crown?
14. In horse racing, what is a maiden?
15. In show-jumping, how many penalty points are given for a refusal?
16. Where is the Royal Hunt Cup run?
17. Which famous horse race, run in October, was

instituted at Newmarket in 1839 in honour of a state visit of the Russian who became Tsar Alexander II?

18. What is the name of the first big horse race of the English flat season run at Doncaster over a straight mile at the end of March?

19. Who was the first woman to ride in the Grand National?

20. How many penalty points are given for a refusal in Cross Country?

Sport : Motor Sports

1. Where was the first British Grand Prix held in 1926?

2. In sports-car racing, how long does the Grand Prix of Endurance last at Le Mans in France?

3. Francorchamps is the most important race track in which country?

4. What name did Sir Malcolm Campbell christen the car in which he broke the World Land Speed Records in 1928 and 1931?

5. Pit Straight, Big Bend, Lesmo Bend and Roggia Bend are parts of which famous motor racing circuit?

6. What does the yellow flag mean in motor racing?

7. What is the name of the American motor sport where the aim is to achieve the highest speed in a straight line over a short distance?

8. What is the name of the world's most famous car rally, which is held annually?

9. Who won 25 Grand Prix, and World Drivers' Championships in 1963 and 1965, before sliding off the track at Hockenheim and receiving fatal injuries?

10. The British Grand Prix is held in alternate years on two British racing car circuits. Silverstone is one –

what is the name of the other?

11. One of the most successful motor-cyclists of all time was Giacomo Agostini who won 12 World Championship titles between 1966 and 1972. What nationality was he?

12. What is the name of America's most famous motor race, which was first held in 1911?

13. Which famous motor racing circuit has places on it named Copse, Maggotts, Becketts and Hanger Straight?

14. What is the name of the resort town of north-east Florida which is known for its motor speed trials on the beach?

Sport : Olympics

1. What do the symbols on the Olympic flag represent?

2. Which sprinter forfeited his gold medal at the 1988 Olympics after being found to have taken steroids?

3. The Olympic Games have only once been held south of the Equator. Where?

4. In what year between the First and Second World Wars were the Olympic Games held in Paris?

5. How many nations took part in the first modern Olympics of 1896?

6. In what year was the XXIII Olympiad held in Los Angeles?

7. Which Olympic event had its first formal contest at the Stockholm Olympic Games in 1912?

8. Who were involved in the tumble upset in the 1984 Olympic Women's 3,000 metres final?

9. How many countries were represented at the 1972 Olympic Games in Munich?

10. In which year was the first women's marathon run in the Olympic Games?
11. In which two years in the first half of the twentieth century were the Olympic Games held in London?
12. Who was the founder of the modern Olympic Games?
13. In which year was judo introduced into the Olympic programme?
14. Eddie the Eagle became famous at the 1988 Calgary Winter Olympics. In which event did he take part?
15. Name the venue of the 1992 Olympic Games.
16. In which year were the first Winter Olympic Games held in Chamonix in France?
17. Who was America's first important swimmer who won five medals, including three golds, at the 1904 Olympics and a gold and a bronze at the 1908 London Olympics?
18. Who won the men's gold medal for ice figure skating at the 1980 Winter Olympic Games?

Sport : Rugby

1. What is the popular term used for rugby union players from New Zealand?
2. How many players are there in a Rugby League Team?
3. What name is given to France's touring side in Rugby Union?
4. In which year was Rugby League's Challenge Cup first held?
5. What is the name of the headquarters of Welsh Rugby Union and has been, since 1954, the venue for all Welsh Home Internationals?
6. Name the two teams who competed in the final of the

Rugby World Cup competition in 1991.

7. The height of the crossbar on a soccer goal is 8 feet or 2.44 metres above the ground but at what height from the ground is a rugby goal crossbar?

8. The British Rugby Union's overseas sides are known as The Lions. From what do they take this name?

9. In Rugby Union, from which country comes the team known as the Pumas?

10. By what popular nickname are the representative Rugby Union teams of Australia known?

11. What name is given to the South African Rugby Football team?

Sport : Tennis

1. Which tennis champion of the 1930s once trained with the Arsenal football team?

2. Martina Navratilova has been a multiple Wimbledon Championship winner. She became an American citizen but in which country was she born?

3. Who was the first American since Tony Trabert in 1955 to win the French Open Tennis Championships in 1989? He was also one of the youngest winners of the title.

4. The All England Club is the most influential of all lawn tennis clubs. By what name was it known in 1869?

5. Name the tennis player who won the Men's Singles title at Wimbledon in 1988 when the match had to be played over two days due to rain.

6. Which British tennis star said in 1968, 'Winners aren't popular, losers often are'?

7. Who won a 'Golden Slam' in 1988 by winning the

singles titles at the Australian, French, Wimbledon and United States tennis championships as well as at the Olympic Games?

8. In Britain in lawn tennis we refer to the additional four feet six inches on each side of the court in doubles as tramlines. What are these sometimes called in the United States?

9. Which Swedish tennis player won the Men's Single title at the Wimbledon Championships for five successive years between the years 1976 and 1980, inclusive?

10. In tennis, what name is given to the women's World Cup?

11. What name is given to a score of 40–40 in tennis?

12. Name the players who appeared in the first all-German Men's Singles tennis final at Wimbledon in 1991.

Sport : Various

1. In archery, what is known as a perfect end?
2. Which three distinct skills make up the game of baseball?
3. How many players are there in a hockey team?
4. In billiards, how many points do you get for a cannon?
5. Who was the first man to swim the English Channel in 1875?
6. In climbing, what is known as a munro?
7. In yachting, what is a metal mike?
8. How many hoops are used in a game of croquet?
9. Why was Susan Brown significant in the 1981 win by Oxford of the annual University Boat Race?

10. The annual Vasa Ski Race attracts thousands of entrants. In which country is it held?
11. What is the maximum possible break in snooker?
12. What is the name of the long staff with an iron tip used in mountaineering?
13. How many players are there in a netball team?
14. How did the game of badminton gain its name?
15. On a dartboard, what number is directly opposite 20?
16. Name the three weapons used in modern fencing.
17. What is the difference between a men's and a women's lacrosse team?
18. The sport of free-style skiing, an acrobatic form of short ski-jumping, is now internationally recognised. By what unusual name was this unusual sport first known?
19. Name the five colours of an archery target starting from the centre.
20. In basketball, how many points are scored each time a player shoots the ball into the basket?
21. How many players are there in a water polo team?
22. In snooker, what value is given to the pink ball?
23. How many players are there in a handball team?
24. The Three Stars is the national ice-hockey team of which country?
25. How many players are there in a rounders team?
26. Name the three lifts in competitive powerlifting.
27. In baseball, what word is used to describe the warm-up enclosure for pitchers and batters, just off the diamond and near the dug-out?
28. How many players are there in a curling team?
29. What boxing weight class falls between bantam-weight and light-weight?
30. What is the maximum number of men allowed on a tug-of-war team?

Sports : Events & Trophies

1. Why is the Calcutta Cup for rugby so named?
2. Which famous sport's cup was stolen in 1966 and was later found by a dog?
3. What type of sporting event do you associate with the annual Calgary Stampede?
4. The King George V Gold Cup and Queen Elizabeth II Gold Cup are major competitions in which sport?
5. Which sport would you be playing if you aimed to win the Lance Todd Memorial Trophy?
6. With what sporting event do you associate Putney and Mortlake?
7. The Sam Maguire Trophy is the major competition in which sport?
8. How often are the World Championships held in netball?
9. In which sport do teams compete for the Federation Cup?
10. Which sport had its first world championship in Yugoslavia in 1951?
11. Which sport is played for the Corbillon Cup?
12. The Caulfield Cup is a major race in which sport?
13. How often are the World Championships held in water skiing?
14. The Grand Challenge Cup is a major competition in which sport?
15. The Silver Broom Trophy is competed for annually in which sport?
16. With which sport do you associate the James Norris Trophy?

17. What type of races are the Cook Strait and Atlantic City Marathon?
18. The Five Nations Championship is a major competition in which sport?
19. Name the most important greyhound race in England known as The Courser's Derby.
20. Which sport do you associate with the Drysdale Cup?
21. In which sport is the Eisenhower trophy competed for by teams?
22. The America's Cup is a yachting trophy, originally presented in 1851. Why is it so called?
23. The Schneider Trophy was contested between the years 1913 and 1931 and Britain, by winning in the last three years, won the trophy outright. Who or what contested for the trophy?
24. With which sport do you associate the Dutch Open, the Coral Mediterranean Open and the St Patrick's Day Singles?

Sports : General

1. The WG Grace Gates were erected in 1923. Where?
2. What is another name for natation?
3. Game birds are protected by the Game Laws from indiscriminate slaughter. Between which dates can grouse not be shot?
4. In which winter holiday resort is the famous bob-sleigh track known as the Cresta Run situated?
5. By what name is Edson Arantes do Nascimento better known?
6. Which sportsman said, 'In my sport the quick are too often listed among the dead'?
7. Approximately how long is the London to Brighton

road walking race, which has been held annually since 1919?

8. What is the meaning of the word karate?
9. Where would you find a baulk line, the 'D' and pyramid spot?
10. What was the name of the game, closely related to cricket, which was played particularly at Easter (a season of courtship)?
11. Where in Scotland would you find the principal winter sports centre in Great Britain?
12. What is the name given to the log which is tossed in an event in The Highland Games?
13. An Irish game, similar to the Scottish sport of shinty, is played with a wooden club or stick and a ball. What is the Irish version called?
14. Lacrosse, basketball and five-pin bowling all originated from which country?
15. In falconry, what word is used to describe the falcon's dive on its prey?
16. Who was the founder of Judo?
17. What feat did Robin Knox-Johnstone achieve in 1968–69?
18. What was the nationality of the first runner to win the London marathon two years in succession (1994 and 1995).
19. The world's first enclosed air-conditioned stadium was the Astrodome in America. In which state is it?
20. Pelota is a ball game played with a wicker-work racquet. Where did the sport originate?
21. In rapid-fire pistol shooting, what are the names of the targets that are used?
22. What is the name of the outdoor game where the aim is to encircle a peg in the ground with an iron ring?
23. What do the initials ITF mean?
24. How many players of an American football team are allowed on the field at one time?

Sports : Sporting Terms

1. In which sport would you hear of a roundhouse, knuckler and outcurve?
2. In which sport is the name of each period of play divided into chukkers (or chukkas)?
3. In which sport are the following moves performed: Triffus, Miller and Rudolf?
4. In which sport might you use a Driving Mashie and a Spade Mashie?
5. In which sport might you have a hog, kiggle-kaggle and pot-lid?
6. In which sport would you find the following terms used: inner, outer and magpie?
7. In which sport would you hear the following terms used: backpedal, purse and uppercut?
8. In which sport are the following terms used: single axle, triple salko and butterfly?
9. With which sport do you associate the Liffey Descent?
10. In what sport are the terms serve, dig and spike used?
11. In which sport are prime, tierce and octave defensive positions?
12. In which sport is the jargon term 'office manager' used?
13. In which sport do the players use a tab, bracer and chestguard?
14. In what sport are the terms tip-off and double-dribble used?
15. In what sport are the terms spares and strikes used?
16. In which sport would you use the following terms:

christies, traversing and edging?
17. In which sport would you find the term chinamen used?
18. In which sport is a Reuther board used?
19. In which sport would you use the term face-off?
20. In which sport is a piton used?
21. In which game would you hear the following words used: bird, kill, smash and lob?
22. In what sport is the descriptive term 'catching a crab' used?

Sports : Which Sport?

1. With which sport do you connect the resort of Klosters?
2. Which sport would you expect to see taking place at Badminton House in Gloucestershire?
3. The New York Knickerbockers (1845) were the first organised team for which sport?
4. If you had entered the Diamond Sculls in what sport would you be participating?
5. What is the sport which originated in Spain and is played with a scoop basket? It is reputed to be the fastest ball-game in the world.
6. What sport takes place in a velodrome?
7. With what sport is Bisley in Surrey associated?
8. What is known as the sport of kings?
9. It is a sport of Oriental origin which took its name from the Tibetan word for ball. It is remarkable in that no one who is left-handed is allowed to participate. What sport is it?
10. With which sport do you associate the Los Angeles Kings?

11. Which sport was pioneered by John MacGregor of Scotland in 1865?

12. Which sport, developed by the American George Nissen, had its first championships in 1948, though it had been used in show business since 1910?

13. Toxophily is a popular world-wide sport – by what name is it more commonly known?

14. In Great Britain the highest one is at Leadhills in Lanarkshire, the longest one at Troon in Ayrshire, and the sport was banned in Scotland for a time. Now, however, its participants receive some of the richest rewards in sport. What sport is it?

15. With which sport do you associate Londonbridge Road in Dublin?

Theatre : Actors & Performers

1. Whose only line in his first play was, 'Tennis anyone'?

2. Who was the first music hall artist to be knighted in 1919 for his contribution to the war effort?

3. For what branch of theatrical art is Marcel Marceau best known?

4. What was the stage name of the British comedian Robert Winthrop (1896–1968)?

5. Which famous French actress, renowned for her tragic roles, continued on the stage, even after having her leg amputated in 1915?

6. He was originally christened Tommy Hicks but changed his name to become a well-known British singer and entertainer. Name him.

7. In 1982, who was the first actress to be portrayed on a British postage stamp?

8. Which British Prima Ballerina's autobiography was

called *Come Dance With Me* (1957)?

9. What was the pseudonym used by Erich Weiss (1874–1926)?

10. Which English actor is famous for his bequest of £3 per annum to be distributed in cake and wine in the Green Room at Drury Lane?

11. Which Australian actor made the character Dame Edna Everidge internationally famous?

12. Which Russian ballet dancer of the Kirov School sought political asylum in the West while he was appearing in Paris in 1961?

13. Who was created a Baron in 1970, thus making him the first theatrical lord?

14. Which music hall comedian's catchphrase was, 'You lucky people'?

15. What was the name of the French rope performer who crossed Niagara Falls on a tight-rope?

16. Which entertainer was known as The Man with the Golden Trumpet?

17. Which actress, originally known as Gladys Smith, became famous as America's Sweetheart?

18. What name did the great ballerina Lilian Alicia Marks adopt?

19. By what name was the Russian Nicolai Poliakoff better known?

20. What was the stage-name of the famous 19th century British actor John Brodribb?

21. Which actor was born Joe Yule Jnr in 1920?

22. By what name was the American jazz singer Eleanora Fagan known?

23. Thrift was the main theme of which famous American comedian's repertoire?

24. Who was the French singer known as The Little Sparrow?

25. She was born Margarete Gertrude Zelle and was a dancer in Paris during the First World War. Found guilty of spying for the Germans she was shot by the French. By what name was she better known?

26. What were the Christian names of the classic comedy duo Burns and Allen?
27. What was the stage-name of the British actor, manager, composer I N Davies, who was known for his musical plays such as *King's Rhapsody* (1949) and *Gay's the Word* (1951)?
28. What was the name of the Russian ballerina for whom Folkine created *The Dying Swan* role?

Theatre : General

1. What is known as the actors' Bible?
2. What was the name of the famous Paris music hall which excelled in lighting and scenic effects and produced spectacular shows – often slightly naughty?
3. With which place do you associate The Passion Play, which is performed every ten years, with over 400 local performers?
4. In the theatre, what name is given to an extravagant comedy based on the tortuous manipulation of situation, rather than wit?
5. In the theatre world, for what do the initials RADA stand?
6. What name is given to the annual awards by the League of New York Theatres to actors and authors for plays on Broadway?
7. Whose circus was known as *The Greatest Show On Earth*?
8. In Italian comedy, who is Harlequin's sweetheart?
9. Michael Crawford played Frank Spencer in *Some Mothers Do 'Ave 'Em*. What Lloyd Webber West End theatre show gave him a major singing role?
10. In the theatre, what is the name used for an actor who

is playing more than one part?

11. Which musical concerns the life of an Argentinian dictator's wife?

12. Name the famous theatre in Dublin founded for plays written by Irish playwrights and performed by Irish actors.

13. It is said to be unlucky to wish an actor good luck on an opening night. What is the usual alternative?

14. What is the name of the narrow platform above the stage from which stagehands adjust scenery?

15. Name the famous octagonal-shaped London Theatre built around 1599 in which Shakespeare acted and later became a shareholder.

16. Who was the founder of the Theatre Workshop in Manchester?

17. What, in 1981, became the then highest-insured show in British Theatre history?

18. What is the name of the American equivalent of the British music hall? It was popular from the late 1800s until the advent of talking pictures.

19. Which theatre, opened at Blackfriars in London in 1959, was the first new theatre to be founded in the City of London since Shakespeare's time, and was established largely due to the efforts of the actor Bernard Miles?

20. Where in a theatre would you find the 'flies'?

Theatre : Plays & Playwrights

1. Who wrote *Death Of A Salesman*?

2. *The Lady's Not For Burning* was one of the witty verse plays by which English dramatist?

3. Which versatile playwright do you associate with *The*

Caretaker and *The Birthday Party*?

4. In which of Noel Coward's plays do you meet Elyot Chase, the divorced husband of Amanda?

5. Which playwright's autobiography was entitled *A Better Class of Person*?

6. Who became an American celebrity with the publication of his play entitled *A Streetcar Named Desire*?

7. Which British author wrote the play *The Admirable Crichton*, a comedy in four acts?

8. How many plays did Shakespeare write?

9. The play entitled *The Mousetrap* was a major success worldwide. Who wrote it?

10. Who wrote the Irish classic play *Cock-a-Doodle Dandy*?

11. *Bedroom Farce, Absent Friends* and *Absurd Person Singular* were all plays by which modern playwright?

12. Who was the Scandinavian dramatist who wrote a play called *The Doll's House*?

13. Which Restoration dramatist's plays include *The Way Of The World* and *Love For Love*?

14. Which playwright had success with *Rosencrantz and Guildenstern are Dead*?

15. Estragon and Vladimir are the two central characters in which tragi-comedy by Samuel Beckett?

16. Which playwright said, 'The trouble with him is that he is in love with his wife and an actor can only afford to be in love with himself'?

17. Which dramatist and short story writer wrote *The Cherry Orchard* and *The Three Sisters*?

18. *Chicken Soup with Barley, I'm Talking About Jerusalem* and *Love Letters on Blue Paper* were all by which playwright?

19. Which playwright commented, 'There's always something fishy about the French'?

20. What was the name of the lady who continuously confused words to comic effect in Sheridan's play *The Rivals*?

21. *Anna Christie* was one of which playwright's early

successes?

22. Which modern writer do you associate with the plays, *Bar-Mitzvah Boy, The Evacuees* and *Spend, Spend, Spend*?

23. The love story of Elizabeth Barrett and Robert Browning was the subject of the play, *The Barretts of Wimpole Street*. Who wrote this play?

24. *A Collier's Friday Night, The Daughter-in-Law* and *The Widowing of Mrs Holroyd* were plays by which author?

25. Roebuck Ramsden Octavius Robinson, Ann Whitefield and John Tanner are all characters from which comic play by George Bernard Shaw?

26. *The Linden Tree* was among the later plays of which writer?

27. Who wrote the autobiographical play *The Glass Menagerie*?

28. Who wrote *The Winslow Boy*?

Transport

1. What was the name of the first Rolls Royce?

2. On the maps of the London Underground, which railway lines are denoted by brown and green respectively?

3. In 1785 Jean Pierre Blanchard and Dr John J Jeffries made an historic crossing of the English Channel – how did they travel?

4. In which year did the Ministry of Transport (now the Department of the Environment) driving test come into force?

5. What name is given to the instrument used for recording flight data in planes?

6. How did the jeep gain its name?

7. Who, in March 1961, was appointed to head British Rail and supervised the savage cuts in the railway network in 1963?

8. Since 1961 the terms Veteran and Vintage have been internationally recognised. How do you distinguish between them?

9. Which European city is served by Charles de Gaulle and Orly airports?

10. In what sphere of human activity did George Pullman achieve everlasting fame?

11. On the last day of December 1968 the first supersonic airliner took to the air. In which country did this take place?

12. What is the name of the machine on the dashboard of a truck which records the vehicle's speed and the length of time the driver has been at the wheel?

13. What origins did the motor car manufacturing firms Bristol and Saab share?

14. What was the name of Laker Airways' cheap transatlantic service inaugurated on 26th September 1977?

15. What name is given to the light two-wheeled hooded vehicle drawn by a man or men first used in Japan around 1870?

16. In which year did the Boeing 747 enter service?

17. Name the first Railway hotels which were opened in London in September 1839.

18. Which car was nicknamed the Tiddler and the Baby Austin?

19. What kind of aircraft is a Chinook?

20. If an aeroplane carried the initials KLM, what international airline would it represent?

21. Who is the only person in the UK allowed to use a motor-car without number plates?

22. What is the principal distinguishing feature of a funicular railway which makes it differ from an ordinary railway system?

23. Which new aeroplane entered scheduled service in

Britain in 1976?

24. What was the name of the first diesel-engined private car to be marketed in 1936?

25. Name the make of car used in the famous St Valentine's Day Masssacre of 14th February 1929 in Chicago.

26. Sir Nigel Gresley designed a steam engine in 1935 which was to establish a world speed record of 126 mph for a steam traction engine in 1938. What was the name of the locomotive?

27. Which British city is served by the airport called Aldergrove?

28. The MG motor-car was one of the most successful makes of British sports and touring cars. For what did the letters MG stand?

29. What do the initials SNCF mean?

30. Which was London's first main line terminus for trains running between London and Birmingham?

Wars & Warfare :
The First & Second World Wars

1. The Germans called this World War I sea battle the Battle of the Skagerrak. What did the British call it?

2. Who was Hitler's deputy from 1933, who was sentenced to life imprisonment at the Nuremberg trials in 1946?

3. What part of the United Kingdom was invaded and occupied by German forces in World War II?

4. Who was the English nurse in Brussels in World War I who was shot by the Germans for helping Allied soldiers to escape?

5. Which incident on 7th December 1941 precipitated the entry of the United States of America into World War II?

6. What name was given to the suicide pilots of the Japanese Air Force in the Second World War.

7. Name three European nations which remained neutral during the course of the Second World War?

8. What benefit did Poland gain from The Polish Corridor which was agreed after the First World War?

9. In World War I, what weapon was used for the first time by Britain in the Battle of Flers-Courcellete in the Somme Offensive?

10. In World War II, what were paravanes used for?

11. What contribution did Reginald Joseph Mitchell make to Britain's war effort in World War II?

12. What was the name of the French resistance movement during World War II?

13. On 7 May 1915 a passenger liner was sunk by an enemy submarine off the coast of Ireland with the loss of 1,200 lives. What was the name of the ship?

14. Name the German battleship which sunk *The Hood* in May 1941 only to be sunk itself a few days later.

15. At the outbreak of World War II what was the name of the French defensive line on their Eastern Boundary with Germany?

16. The Germans code-named it Operation Barbarossa – planned in 1940 and carried out in 1941. What was Barbarossa?

17. He was a Dutchman who died in 1939. During the First World War he designed very successful German military aircraft – who was he?

18. What kind of aircraft was the Second World War Horsa?

19. Which British warship was sunk by German submarines whilst at anchor in Scapa Flow during the Second World War?

20. The armistice which was signed to conclude hostilities in the First World War was signed in unusual

surroundings. Where?

21. It was originally known as the Local Defence Volunteer Force when formed early in World War II. To what was its name changed?
22. Which kind of aircraft was used in the famous dambusting air-raid, led by Guy Gibson, in May 1943?
23. Whose portrait was used in the famous First World War recruiting poster with the quotation, 'Your Country Needs You'?
24. Apart from being towns in Britain, what significance did Stirling, Sunderland, Manchester, Lancaster and Halifax have in World War II?
25. A meeting took place between Churchill, Stalin and Roosevelt during the Second World War to decide the fate of Europe after the fall of Hitler's Germany. Where did this meeting take place?
26. Who was in command of the British Fleet at the Battle of Jutland in the First World War when the Germans suffered a major naval defeat?
27. What town, famous for its mineral water, acquired additional fame as the capital of unoccupied France in 1940?
28. Who was the Supreme Allied Commander of the Allied Expeditionary Forces in Western Europe in 1943–45 during the Second World War?

Wars & Warfare :
Other Wars

1. Who commanded the British forces against Quebec in 1759, captured the town but lost his life in the battle?
2. In which war were fought the battles of Sinope, Alma

and Inkerman between 1853 and 1854?

3. At his infamous Last Stand in 1876, how many men is General George Armstrong Custer said to have had under his command?

4. In which war was Britain engaged during the years 1899–1902?

5. Who was Britain's second-in-command at the Battle of Copenhagen in 1801?

6. Where did the Boxer Rising take place between 1898 and 1900?

7. Which Scottish regiment, because of its heroic bravery against formidable odds in the Crimean War, earned the nickname The Thin Red Line?

8. Who was the Moslem warrior who defended the Holy Land against the Christian Knights during the 3rd Crusade?

9. Which was the last battle of the Wars of the Roses in which Richard III was defeated and killed?

10. Which war took place between the years 1950–1953?

11. Which war was brought to an end by the surrender of forces under the command of General Cornwallis?

12. Which war took place between 1861–1865?

13. Who was the British General (later Field-Marshal) who was sent to subjugate the Scottish Highlands, which he achieved by building an extensive system of military roads and bridges?

14. In 1816, Chaka, variously described as a sadistic and half-crazed but brilliant military general, became leader of his people and wielded power for over half a century. Who were his people?

15. In which battle of 1644 did Oliver Cromwell defeat Prince Rupert?

16. Which English King was nicknamed The Hammer of the Scots?

17. When did the Vietnam War begin and end?

18. Who was the commander of the Scots Army which defeated the English at the Battle of Bannockburn in 1314?

19. What notable distinction was gained by Lieutenant Charles Lucas – a British naval officer – on 21st June 1854?
20. By what name was the war between 1618–1648, which was really a series of wars, more commonly known?
21. The Mohawk, Oneida, Onandaga, Cayuga and Seneca tribes formed a powerful confederacy of North American Indian tribes who fought for the British against the French. What were these tribes collectively called?
22. A battle took place in 1746 near Inverness where the Duke of Cumberland's army defeated the forces of Bonnie Prince Charlie. What was the battle called?
23. The bronze guns captured by the British from the Russians at Sebastapol in 1855 were melted down and used over a period of time for a very special purpose. What purpose?
24. What was the name of the battle of 1690 where William III of England with 35,000 troops routed his rival James II with 21,000 men ending Stuart hopes of regaining the throne?
25. Who commanded the Indian forces at the Battle of the Little Big Horn?
26. The English Civil War raged between 1642 and 1646, from disputes between Parliament and the King. Which king?
27. In which war did Paul Revere become a national hero?

Wars & Warfare : Various

1. What name is given to the knife which the Gurkha soldiers are famous for?
2. What is the highest commissioned rank in the Royal

Air Force?

3. What is the date of Armistice Day?
4. In which castle would you find the piece of ordnance called Mons Meg?
5. What weapon is associated with Britannia, Neptune and a gladiator known as Retiarius?
6. What is the name of the Queen's bodyguard in Scotland?
7. Lollius Urbicus was responsible for building a defensive wall to keep out Scottish tribes. What was it called?
8. Why was the poppy chosen as the flower for Remembrance Sunday?
9. How many pips has a lieutenant in the British Army?
10. Which European country is sometimes called The Cock-pit of Europe because of the many battles and wars fought on its soil?
11. What is the RAF slang for the electrical distributor which releases bombs from aircraft?
12. What is the name of Britain's only private army?
13. What was the name of Britain's first guided-missile destroyer, which was launched in June 1960?
14. A minuteman is an American missile, but who or what were the original minute men?
15. The Monteneros guerrillas are infamous for their activities in which country?
16. What term is used to describe a neutral country between two others who might go to war?
17. In military jargon, what is the meaning of the abbreviation ABM?

Which Year?

1. The television licence fee was raised from £2 to £3; Roger Bannister ran the first sub four minute mile; and all food rationing ended in Britain. Which year was this?
2. In which year did Britain first have parking meters?
3. Mrs Thatcher was elected leader of the Conservative Party; King Feisal of Saudi Arabia was assassinated and a £6 limit on pay increases was agreed. Which year was this?
4. Nelson Mandela was freed after twenty-seven years in captivity; the trial took place of the Guinness men accused of insider dealing; the Queen Mother celebrated her 90th birthday. Which year was this?
5. Which year is often called The Year of Revolutions because unrest swept through Europe at this time?
6. Jimmy Carter became the 39th President of the USA; Steve Biko died while under arrest; President Sadat became the first Egyptian leader to visit Israel. Which year was this?
7. Severe storms hit the South East of England, during which Kew Gardens lost a third of its trees; the bottom fell out of the Stock Market on the day which was quickly labelled Black Monday; an IRA bomb exploded in Enniskillen, Northern Ireland, just as people gathered for a Remembrance Day Service. Which year was this?
8. £1 million of diamonds were stolen from Christie's; President Andropov died; and Mr Harold MacMillan was awarded an Earldom on his 90th birthday. Which

year was this?

9. In which year did the penny post begin in England?
10. When was the first woman High Court Judge appointed in Great Britain?
11. British and French workers shared champagne when the breakthrough was made in the Channel Tunnel; the Maastricht summit on Europe took place; the last oil fire started during the Gulf War was extinguished. Which year was this?
12. Colour programmes began on BBC1 and ITV; Concorde had its maiden flight; and the voting age became eighteen. Which year was this?
13. In which year were women priests first ordained into the Church of England?
14. In which year did the Great Exhibition open at Crystal Palace?
15. Henry VIII's flagship, *The Mary Rose,* was raised from the Solent's mud; the Pope visited Britain for the first time in 450 years; Princess Grace of Monaco was killed in a car crash; Argentina invaded the Falkland Islands. Which year was this?
16. Martin Luther King was assassinated; the Vietnam peace talks began in Paris; and Senator Robert Kennedy was shot and died in Los Angeles. Which year was this?
17. In which year was the Berlin Wall built?
18. In which year was the Festival of Britain?
19. Which year saw the deaths of Rudolf Nuryev, Audrey Hepburn, Les Dawson and James Hunt?
20. In which year did the British breathalyser law come into force?

Words & Phrases : Meanings

1. What is the meaning of the word 'hi-fi'?
2. What is meant by the jargon phrase 'a dry run' in television?
3. What is the significance of the suffix 'caster' or 'chester' on a British place name?
4. What is the literal meaning of 'papier-mâché'?
5. To which art form is the word 'terpsichorean' applicable?
6. In airline jargon we hear the term 'Apex' used. What does this mean?
7. If an Ordnance Survey map identified a 'tumulus', to what would it be referring.
8. What does the phrase 'open house' mean?
9. 'Tetra' is a prefix used in numerous words, e.g. tetrach, tetrapod and tetrameter. What does 'tetra' mean?
10. If you suffered from pyrophobia, of what would you be frightened?
11. If someone is a somnambulist, what does he do?
12. What names are used to describe a man and a woman who make a Will?
13. Which word is defined as 'the ability to enter into the feelings and sensations of another'?
14. The suffix 'algia' comes from the Greek and is used in many medical terms, e.g. neuralgia. What does algia mean?
15. What is the meaning of the word 'gospel'?
16. What does the word 'hieroglyphics' literally mean?
17. What is meant by the word 'omniscient'?
18. What is the literal meaning of acropolis?

Words & Phrases : Names

1. What is the name of the stimulant found in coffee?
2. What name is often used contemptuously to describe a country bumpkin?
3. What name is given to the horizontal bar which joins the legs of furniture?
4. What name is given to a tenancy of land from year to year or for a term of years?
5. What name is given to a station for helicopter passenger services?
6. What name is given to the independent investigator who protects citizens against maladministration by civil servants?
7. What name is given to a government ruled by women?
8. What name is given to a dead body which is preserved by embalming and is associated with ancient Egypt?
9. What name is given to the icicle-shaped deposits which hang from the roofs of caves in limestone areas?
10. What name describes a piece of verse made up in such a way that when the first letters of the lines are read down the page they make up a word?
11. The British Army has a bugle call for every occasion. What names are given to the first and the last bugle calls of the day?
12. What name is given to the art of telling fortunes by playing cards or by the Tarot pack?
13. What name is used to describe an object which is

worn to charm or ward off evil influences?

14. What name is given to the type of auction where the price of the article is reduced by stages until a buyer is found?

15. What is a person who collects coins called?

16. What name is given to the Japanese custom of suicide, practised when the person is in disgrace?

17. What is the name of the vigorous Spanish style of singing and guitar-playing which is often danced to?

18. The English call them nappies. What do the Americans call them?

19. What name is given to the underground burial places dug out of rock in Rome?

20. What name is given to an attempt to read character from the lines in the hand?

21. What name is given to the upright member in the middle of the back of a chair?

Words & Phrases :
Studies & Occupations

1. What name is given to the study of the system of language sounds?

2. If you studied hippology, what would you be studying?

3. What does an icthyologist study?

4. You might expect to see a funambulist performing in a circus. What would he be doing?

5. What does a palaeontologist study?

6. What name is given to the art of arranging the skins of dead animals, birds and fishes?

7. A cooper is a barrel-maker but what occupation does a coper have?
8. What does a speleologist study?
9. If you were studying coleoptera what would you be examining?
10. What is the common name for the craft known as serigraphy?
11. If a lepidopterist offered to show you his collection what would you see?
12. What is known as Adam's Profession?
13. What is dendrochronology?
14. Entomology is the study of insects – but what is etymology?
15. What is lexicography?

Words & Phrases : Terms

1. What term is synonymous with Cosa Nostra?
2. What is the term for the movement aimed at the unification of Christian Churches?
3. What is the legal term used to describe a written voluntary statement, given under oath?
4. What term is used for the historical study of personal and place names?
5. What term is used to describe a word formed from the same letters as another word?
6. What term describes the colour and feel that wood takes on as a result of age, wear and polishing?
7. What is the legal term used to describe an agreement, often unlawful, between two or more producers, to maintain artificially high prices for their products?
8. What term is used for a poetical lament for (usually) a dead friend?

9. What is the derisive term used for language that is not intelligible by normal standards, for example bureaucratic documents?
10. What is another term for dowsing?
11. What is the legal term used to describe a document under seal whereby a testator can amend, alter or amplify a will previously made?
12. What term is used to describe a person appointed to vote in place of another?
13. What term is used to describe the art of drawing maps?
14. What term is used to describe a period of leave granted to members of staff, often in recognition of long service, or for some period of travel and study?
15. What term describes a court case that is held in a private room away from the public?
16. Which legal term is used to describe a writ, directed to an individual, requiring him to attend and give evidence?

Words & Phrases :
Uses & Origins

1. For what is a mangel-wurzel used?
2. What would a Scotsman do with a spurtle?
3. Why is a bayonet so called?
4. From where does the word POSH come?
5. What would you do with a Wandering Sailor?
6. A thug in the English Language is defined as a ruffian or cut-throat. Who or what were the original thugs?
7. How did the word salary originate?

8. What would you do with daiquiri?
9. From where does the word aphrodisiac come?
10. For what would a 16th or 17th century lady use a farthingale?
11. From where is the word bedlam derived?
12. Why do we call a useless or troublesome gift a white elephant?

Words & Phrases : Various

1. In primitive and tribal cultures, who or what was a shaman?
2. Why is the Volkswagen car so called?
3. What is the slang name given to the control lever of an aeroplane?
4. What would you fear if you had apiphobia?
5. Which word describes death imposed by hanging from a wooden cross?
6. What do you call a small gabled window, projecting from a sloping roof?
7. If you accepted wampum from a Red Indian what would you be receiving?
8. Which word means an assembly of witches?
9. Of what would you be frightened if you suffered from musophobia?
10. Foreman, Longman, Lechman, Littleman and Thuma are always found together. Why?
11. What is the singular of scampi?
12. In which part of the United Kingdom is a judge known as a deemster?
13. Of what is the word gin an abbreviation?
14. Where would you find firedamp?

15. What is the opposite of the word "nadir"?
16. What is remarkable about the construction of the word facetious?

Words & Phrases : What is it?

1. What is an umiak?
2. What is Muckle Flugga?
3. What is an Annie Oakley?
4. What is a runcible spoon?
5. The shipworm is not a worm. What is it?
6. What is a saraband?
7. What is a turnstone?
8. What is a ha-ha?
9. What is majolica?
10. What is a death cap?
11. What is a harmattan?
12. What is a Catherine Wheel?
13. What is a firkin?
14. What is an appaloosa?
15. What is a cabana?
16. What is a greengage?
17. Who or what is a doppelganger?
18. What is a nest egg?
19. What is a felucca?
20. What is a hookah?
21. What is a spinet?
22. Who or what is a guppy?
23. What is a skua?
24. What is Yaws?
25. What is a zither?
26. What is a Suffolk Punch?

27. The Light-house of the Mediterranean is not a light-house at all. What is it?
28. What is a cassowary?
29. What is a basenji?
30. What is a ziggurat?
31. What are Walloons?
32. What is a Lee Enfield?
33. What is a grouper?
34. What is a mandrill?
35. What is a Kerry Blue?
36. What is Dorset Blue Vinney?
37. Who or what is a Portuguese Man of War?
38. What is a runnel?
39. What is a devil's coach horse?
40. What is an ayah?
41. What is a hula?
42. What is a drupe?

Answers

 1. Amateur Athletic Association.
 2. British Library Automated Information Service.
 3. Association of British Travel Agents.
 4. Association of Cinematograph, Television and Allied Technicians.
 5. In the year of our Lord.
 6. Acquired Immune Deficiency Syndrome.
 7. Australian and New Zealand Army Corps.
 8. Advanced Passenger Train.
 9. Auxiliary Territorial Service.
10. Airborne Warning And Control System.
11. British Academy of Film and Television Arts.
12. Beginners All Purpose Symbolic Instruction Code.
13. The dentist (British Dental Association).
14. British Summer Time.
15. Campaign Against Racial Discrimination.
16. Common Business Oriented Language.
17. Council for the Preservation of Rural England.
18. District of Columbia.
19. Director of Public Prosecutions.
20. Distinguished Service Order and Distinguished Flying Cross.
21. Department of Social Security.
22. Driver and Vehicle Licensing Centre.
23. Ear, Nose and Throat.
24. Electro-Plated Nickel Silver.
25. Electronic Random Number Indicator Equipment.
26. Extra-Sensory Perception.
27. The British Association of Accountants and Auditors.
28. Fellow of the Institute of Chartered Accountants.
29. Architects.
30. Veterinary Surgeons.
31. Government Issue (as marked on many American supplies).
32. Her (or His) Majesty's Stationery Office.
33. Intelligence Quotient.
34. International Olympic Committee.
35. King's Own Scottish Borderers.

36. Member of the European Parliament.
37. Missile Defence Alarm System.
38. Navy, Army and Air Force Institutes.
39. National Aeronautics and Space Administration.
40. North Atlantic Treaty Organisation.
41. Organisation of Petroleum-Exporting Countries.
42. Polyvinyl chloride.
43. Quasi-autonomous Non-Governmental Organisation.
44. Royal Academy of Dramatic Art.
45. Royal Society for the Prevention of Cruelty to Animals.
46. Répondez s'il vous plaît (please reply).
47. International Standard Book Number.
48. Society for the Promotion of Christian Knowledge.
49. South-East Asia Treaty Organisation.
50. Television and Infra-Red Observation Satellite.
51. Trinitrotoluene (high explosive).
52. Train de Grande Vitesse (high speed train).
53. Unidentified Flying Object.
54. United Nations Educational, Scientific and Cultural Organisation.
55. The relief of children in emergencies (United Nations International Children Emergencies Fund).
56. Very Important Person.
57. Very high frequency.
58. Vertical Take-Off and Landing.
59. Youth Hostels Association.
60. Young Men's Christian Association.

Animal World: Names
1. Kiwi.
2. A farm horse.
3. Bee Hummingbird.
4. Rodents.
5. A legless lizard.
6. Adder.
7. Schnauzer.
8. Sheep.
9. Swarm.
10. Stormy Petrel.
11. The Yak.
12. Dog.
13. Cob (male) and Pen (female).
14. The human flea.
15. Maggots.
16. Dachshund.

17. The Connemara.
18. Huskies.
19. Daddy-longlegs.
20. A jenny.
21. Armadillo.
22. A joey.
23. The owl.
24. Mule.
25. A drone.
26. Airedale.
27. Barbary Ape.
28. Ferret.
29. The salmon.
30. The Shire horse.
31. Eyas.
32. An antelope.
33. A leveret.
34. The giant squid.
35. Reindeer or caribou.
36. Alpaca.
37. Jersey and Guernsey.
38. Crab.
39. The Royal Bengal Tiger.
40. Chipmunk.
41. The camel.
42. Dromedary and Bactrian.

Animal World: Physical Matters
1. Four.
2. Five.
3. Head – Thorax – Abdomen.
4. Ten.
5. Scut.
6. Black.
7. It would have hooves.
8. Nine months.
9. Highest part of its withers – base of crest-line of its neck.
10. Merino.
11. Goat skin.
12. Ten.
13. Five.
14. A long nose.
15. Sheep (sometimes from a horse or ass).
16. By beating their wings.
17. Twenty-one months.

18. They hunt by sight.
19. Plumage.

Animal World: The Most
 1. Malarial Mosquitoes.
 2. The Blue Whale.
 3. The Death Puffer.
 4. The Ostrich.
 5. The House Mouse.
 6. The Common Lizard.
 7. The Irish Wolfhound.
 8. The Wandering Albatross.
 9. The Sperm Whale.
10. The Giant Tortoise.
11. The Roe Deer.
12. The Slow-worm.

Animal World: What Is It?
 1. A desert rattlesnake.
 2. A type of elephant (now extinct).
 3. The rabbit.
 4. Ants.
 5. A breed of toy dog.
 6. A large flightless bird.
 7. The Dragonfly.
 8. Marine mammals like sea-cows.
 9. A variety of Welsh corgi with a long tail.
10. Cattle with no horns.
11. A kind of fresh-water tortoise.
12. Pigeons or doves.
13. A lizard.
14. Shrew.
15. A small wild dog.
16. A scaly ant-eater.
17. A pig. (A ferocious long-legged wild variety.)
18. An Australian snake.
19. A web-footed bird.
20. A horse. (Smallest horse in the world, bred in Argentina).
21. A mongoose.
22. A toad.
23. A monkey.
24. Turkeys.
25. The aardvark.
26. The wolf.

27. A parrot.
28. An antelope.
29. A member of the bat family.
30. The Sandpipers.
31. A large wild goat (found in the Himalayas).
32. The capercaillie.
33. Amphibians.
34. Bats.
35. The thrush family.

Animal World: Where In The World?
1. Australia.
2. North America.
3. Vienna.
4. Netherlands.
5. Australia.
6. In South America.
7. Cairngorm Mountains, Scotland.
8. Wales.
9. India.
10. Mexico.
11. Australia. (A marsupial, like a large rat.)
12. America.

Art
1. Sandro Botticelli.
2. Georges Seurat.
3. El Greco.
4. John Constable.
5. Claude Monet.
6. Sir Jacob Epstein.
7. J M W Turner.
8. Impressionist.
9. Renoir.
10. Sir Joshua Reynolds.
11. Salvador Dali.
12. London and Venice.
13. Vincent Van Gogh.
14. Frans Hals.
15. Graham Sutherland.
16. James Whistler.
17. Canaletto.
18. *The Mona Lisa*.
19. Pablo Picasso.

20. Jan Van Eyck.
21. Andy Warhol.
22. Pieter Brueghel.
23. Paintings of animals.
24. Camille Pissarro.
25. Miniatures.
26. Henry Moore.
27. Sir John Everett Millais.
28. Van Dyck.
29. Sidney Nolan.
30. Giovanni Bellini.
31. Henri de Toulouse Lautrec.
32. Rembrandt.
33. *The Toilet of Venus*.
34. Tahiti.
35. Michelangelo.
36. Raphael.
37. Henri Matisse.
38. Pierre Renoir.
39. Leonardo da Vinci.
40. Titian.
41. Pieter de Hooch.
42. Gainsborough.
43. Animals – particularly horses.
44. Ruskin Spear.
45. The Little Mermaid.
46. Jean Francois Millet.
47. Sir Edwin Henry Landseer.
48. Stanley Spencer.
49. Auguste Rodin.
50. Giovanni Bellini.
51. Edgar Degas.
52. Eros.
53. Over the entrance of BBC Broadcasting House, London.
54. Cubism.

The Arts
1. Marquetry.
2. Medici.
3. Ballet – he founded the Russian Ballet Company.
4. The Sistine Chapel in Rome.
5. Elgin Marbles.
6. Lace.
7. Art Deco.
8. El Greco.

9. A torch.
10. Isodora Duncan.
11. On the toes.
12. The Louvre, Paris.
13. Toulouse Lautrec.
14. Sir Joshua Reynolds.
15. The Crystal Palace – later re-erected at Sydenham.
16. Antwerp.
17. Alcazar.
18. A residence of French kings.
19. The Tate Gallery.
20. Rio de Janeiro.
21. Michelangelo.
22. Pieta.
23. He drew a perfect freehand circle with a sweep of his arm.
24. Surrealism.
25. Purple.
26. Spain.
27. Prado.
28. Christ In Glory.
29. Sculpture.
30. Architecture and stage and costume design.
31. Linseed oil.
32. The Eisteddfod.
33. Origami.
34. Yellow.
35. Sir Christopher Wren.
36. Opera.
37. Clipping hedges into artistic shapes.
38. Equity.
39. Music – particularly as a pianist.
40. Ikebana.

Astronomy
1. The Apollo Project.
2. Meteors.
3. Jupiter.
4. Southern Crown and Northern Crown.
5. Zenith.
6. 13 (and a small bit).
7. Mariner's Compass.
8. Orion.
9. Asteroids.
10. Mercury.
11. They are some of the brighest stars.

12. Goat.
13. Mars.
14. Neptune.
15. Jodrell Bank.
16. That the Universe came into being as the result of a gigantic explosion.
17. Jupiter.
18. It always points away from the sun.
19. Eclipse.
20. Virgo.
21. Aristotle.
22. Andromeda.
23. Polaris.
24. Between Mars and Jupiter.
25. Ursa Major – The Plough – Charlie's Wain.
26. King Charles II.
27. Colonel Edwin (Buzz) Aldrin.
28. That the Sun was the centre of our Universe – not the Earth.
29. Venus.
30. The twins.
31. Mars.
32. Proxima Centauri.
33. Sagittarius.
34. They are some of the world's largest meteorites.
35. Aurora Borealis.
36. Every 76 years.
37. Ganymede.
38. Milky Way.
39. Earth.
40. Voyager 1.
41. Neptune.
42. Aquarius.
43. Libra (the scales).
44. Black hole.

The Bible
 1. He created the sun, moon and stars.
 2. 36.
 3. A raven.
 4. The lilies of the field.
 5. 3 days and nights.
 6. Gabriel.
 7. Jezebel.
 8. Mount of Olives.
 9. James I of England (VI of Scotland).

10. Deuteronomy.
11. Balthazar, Melchior, Caspar.
12. Noah's Ark.
13. Cedar wood.
14. The fruit of the tree of knowledge of good and evil.
15. Mount Sinai.
16. Aaron.
17. Goliath.
18. Tarsus.
19. Abel.
20. Book of Malachi.
21. Queen of Sheba.
22. St Stephen.
23. Zacharias and Elizabeth.
24. He kissed him so that the soldiers could identify him.
25. Genesis, Exodus, Leviticus, Numbers and Deuteronomy.
26. Armageddon.
27. Tabernacle.
28. Shadrach, Meshach and Abednego.
29. Michael.
30. The head of John the Baptist.
31. Moses.
32. Joachim and Anna.
33. Isaac and Rebekah.
34. Damascus.
35. Sodom and Gomorrah.
36. Noah.
37. Amen.
38. The first five books of the Old Testament.
39. Two fishes (five loaves).
40. Gospels.
41. Jericho.
42. Noah's Ark is said to have come to rest here after the floods abated.
43. Thou shalt have no other gods before me. (Do not worship any other gods.)
44. A mess of pottage.
45. Daniel.
46. Abraham.
47. Christ's feeding of the 5,000 with the loaves and fishes.
48. Olive trees.
49. Pontius Pilate.
50. The Ten Commandments.
51. Exodus.
52. Goliath.
53. Andrew.

54. John the Baptist in the River Jordan.
55. Jacob's.
56. Revelation.

Buildings
 1. Apsley House (now the Wellington Museum).
 2. Windsor Castle.
 3. The Alhambra.
 4. Sir Basil Spence.
 5. The Mermaid.
 6. Kensington Gardens.
 7. The Taj Mahal.
 8. Wells Cathedral.
 9. St Peter's, Rome.
10. A minaret.
11. Windmills.
12. Isambard Kingdom Brunel.
13. Le Corbusier.
14. Norman.
15. Baron Georges Eugene Haussmann.
16. Nave.
17. Robert Adam.
18. The Guild Hall.
19. Martello Towers.
20. Chicago.
21. A detached church bell tower.
22. Perpendicular.
23. A bascule bridge.
24. Canterbury Cathedral.
25. The Great Fire of London.
26. Its stained glass.
27. Coventry Cathedral.
28. Woburn Abbey.
29. Blenheim Palace.
30. Mezzanine.
31. St Giles'.
32. Elysée Palace.
33. Spain.
34. York Minster.
35. The Wedding Cake.
36. Sir Charles Barry.
37. Chequers.
38. Ferdinand de Lesseps.
39. Buckingham Palace.
40. Castle Howard.

41. Belfry.
42. Hampton Court Palace.
43. Lincoln Cathedral.
44. The Pentagon (6½ million square feet).
45. Liverpool (the Catholic Cathedral, opened 1967).
46. Sir Christopher Wren.
47. 102 storeys.
48. Cambridge.
49. The National Gallery.

The Calendar
1. In a leap year.
2. 25th January.
3. 1st July.
4. Lady Day (25th March); Midsummer Day (24th June); Michael-mas Day (29th September) and Christmas Day (25th December).
5. 15th March.
6. Halloween.
7. 7th November.
8. 11th November.
9. 1st May.
10. New Zealand.
11. Saint David's.
12. Marbles.
13. Australia and New Zealand.
14. Thanksgiving Day.
15. Christmas.
16. March.
17. 1st October – 1st February.
18. 15th July.
19. New Year's Eve.
20. November.
21. 4th July.
22. Epiphany.
23. July.
24. Julian (old style); Gregorian (new style).
25. 1st September.

Cartoon Characters
1. He was a rabbit.
2. Flora, Fauna and Merryweather.
3. An alley cat.
4. Donald Duck.
5. Brer Rabbit.

6. Sylvester.
7. Dumbo.
8. Speedy Gonzales.
9. Deputy Dawg.
10. Baloo.
11. A fox. (The sly fox who led Pinocchio the puppet astray.)
12. Bedrock.
13. Doc, Sneezy, Grumpy, Happy, Sleepy, Dopey and Bashful.
14. Snoopy.
15. Bluto.
16. Mickey Mouse.
17. Timothy.
18. Pat Sullivan.
19. Charlie Brown.
20. Garfield.

Common Link
1. All colleges at Cambridge.
2. All famous magicians.
3. All Morris Dances.
4. All bell changes (in bell ringing).
5. All desks.
6. All Clipper ships.
7. All born in Portsmouth.
8. All periods of architecture.
9. All parts of a spinning wheel.
10. All Astronomers Royal.
11. All breeds of chicken.
12. All casks and measures.
13. All road tunnels under the River Thames.
14. All went to Harrow.
15. All oil fields and rigs in the North Sea.
16. All towers in the Tower of London.
17. All card games.
18. All were left-handed.
19. All roses.
20. All types of bean.
21. All places of pilgrimage.
22. All butterflies.
23. All were pacifists.
24. All married before they were 16.
25. All birds which don't fly.
26. All apple trees.
27. All have narrow gauge railways.
28. All Hindu castes.

29. All were American artists.
30. All were famous hangmen.
31. All stud poker games.
32. All buried at Highgate Cemetery.
33. All breeds of sheep.
34. All types of wine glass.
35. All Poets Laureate.
36. All general anaesthetics.
37. All North American Indian Tribes.
38. All types of loaf.
39. All types of nail.
40. All types of chair.

Crime & Punishment
1. The Seventh Earl of Lucan, or Lord Lucan.
2. Dr Hawley Harvey Crippen's.
3. Martin Luther King's.
4. Devil's Island.
5. John Reginald Halliday Christie.
6. She was the last woman to be executed in Britain.
7. It was a noted debtors' prison, notorious for the cruelties inflicted on its prisoners.
8. Arson.
9. The beating of the soles of the feet with thin rods.
10. He was a burglar.
11. Al Capone.
12. George Joseph Smith.
13. A pickpocket.
14. He turned King's evidence.
15. Dick Turpin.
16. Charles Peace.
17. The Boston Strangler.
18. Alcatraz.
19. Sweeney Todd.
20. Jack The Ripper.
21. Bluebeard.
22. The Great Train Robbery.
23. Neck and wrists.
24. Mary Ann Cotton.
25. New Scotland Yard.
26. Lee Harvey Oswald.
27. Botany Bay.
28. Fraud.
29. An acid bath.
30. Sir Francis Galton.

31. Judge Jeffreys.
32. A sword.
33. He poisoned himself with hemlock.
34. John Hinckley.
35. 1964.
36. Henry Fielding (a magistrate at Bow Street Court, London).
37. Colonel Thomas Blood.

Decorations and Emblems

1. The George Cross.
2. Le Tricolour.
3. Order of the Purple Heart.
4. The death of the Sovereign, at the funerals of Prime Ministers and ex-Prime Ministers and by specific royal command.
5. For Valour.
6. The maple leaf.
7. A torch.
8. It is a distress signal.
9. It is not rectangular – it comprises two over-lapping triangles.
10. White and red.
11. Crimson.
12. Six.
13. It is the name of the Rolls-Royce symbol of the flying lady.
14. Lying down – with body resting on legs and head lifted.
15. The Orders of the Garter, the Bath, the Thistle and St Patrick.
16. Five.
17. The Pope – it portrays a picture of St Peter in a boat.
18. St Andrew, St Patrick and St George.
19. Happiness.
20. Iron Cross.
21. Pale blue and white.
22. Lord Lyon King of Arms.
23. The wattle blossom.
24. New Zealand.
25. Denmark's.
26. Accolade (or 'dubbing').
27. Victoria Cross.
28. The flag of the USA.
29. Vietnam's.
30. The pirates' black flag with the skull and cross-bones.

Dress

1. Mary Quant.
2. Red.

3. Tuxedo.
4. On the feet.
5. Gaberdine.
6. Greece.
7. A bride.
8. Honeycomb stitch.
9. A scarf (blue with white dots on it).
10. A large hat with a wide brim, drooping at one side.
11. It is a shortened version of swallowtails (the correct name).
12. Cloaks or capes.
13. The Kipper Tie.
14. Yashmak.
15. A belt with a strap over the right shoulder.
16. Codpiece.
17. A black felt hat.
18. Hobble skirt.
19. Eskimo – anoraque.
20. Christian Dior.
21. A Bishop.
22. Cagoule.
23. Off the west coast of Ireland in the mouth of Galway Bay.
24. Harris Tweed.
25. Mantilla.
26. A soft felt hat.
27. Coco.
28. Chitterlings.
29. Cardigan (after the Earl of Cardigan).
30. A knight – they are all parts of a suit of armour.
31. Lincoln Green.
32. A Poncho.
33. A Sporran.
34. Culottes.
35. Zandra Rhodes.
36. Sir Norman Hartnell.
37. Extremely wide bottomed trousers (1920s).
38. On the head. A nun.

Exploration & Discovery
1. Sir Joseph Banks.
2. El Dorado.
3. Charles Lindbergh.
4. Leif Ericcson.
5. Sputnik 1 and Explorer 1.
6. Prince Henry of Portugal.
7. Wales.

8. George Vancouver.
9. Canton in China.
10. Cape of Good Hope.
11. Angel Falls – the highest waterfall in the world.
12. Magellan.
13. Robert Edwin Peary.
14. Early Bird.
15. Vostok.
16. John Cabot.
17. *Tigris*.
18. Mason and Dixon.
19. Richard Evelyn Byrd.
20. Hawaiian Islands.
21. Genoese (Italian).
22. Robert J Flaherty.
23. Alcock and Brown.
24. Sally Ride.
25. Amerigo Vespucci.
26. Sir Richard Burton.
27. Alec Rose.
28. Captain Bruce McCandless.
29. Roald Amundsen – he was Norwegian.
30. Lake Victoria and the source of the River Nile.
31. Scottish.
32. Apollo Programme.
33. Jacques Cartier.
34. David Livingstone.

Famous People: General
1. Marie Curie.
2. Andrew Carnegie.
3. Thomas Cook.
4. Esperanto (an artificial language for international use).
5. He was blind.
6. Arthur.
7. Lancelot (Capability) Brown.
8. Beau Brummell.
9. He wrote *The Star Spangled Banner* in 1814.
10. Louis Pasteur.
11. Charles Babbage.
12. Piracy (they were both pirates).
13. Grace Darling.
14. Librarian.
15. Quasimodo.
16. Roy Plomley.

17. Thomas (Stonewall) Jackson.
18. John Merrick.
19. Cecil J Rhodes.
20. Frank Winfield Woolworth.
21. Helen Keller.
22. Nicholas Breakspear.
23. Elizabeth Garrett Anderson.
24. Sir Thomas Gresham.
25. John Lennon.
26. Rowland Hill.
27. Her developments in infant education (nursery schools).
28. Ruth Lawrence.
29. Joan of Arc.
30. Sigmund Freud.
31. Leprosy.
32. Nostradamus.
33. Harry Gordon Selfridge (Selfridge's stores).
34. Mother Teresa.
35. General Chiang Kai-Shek.
36. Elizabeth Fry.
37. Valentin Hauy.
38. Flora Macdonald.
39. Evangeline Booth (seventh child of William).
40. The MacGregor or Campbell clan.
41. Pope John Paul II.
42. Florence Nightingale.
43. Richard Dimbleby.
44. Thomas Arnold.
45. Pocahontas.
46. Oliver Cromwell.
47. He was a teacher of deaf and dumb children.
48. Thomas Malthus.

Famous People: The World of Politics
 1. General Fulgencia Batista.
 2. She was the first woman MP in Britain.
 3. Law. (He was a lawyer.)
 4. Martin Luther King.
 5. James Keir Hardie.
 6. Emily Davison.
 7. John Adams.
 8. David Lloyd George.
 9. Francois Duvalier.
10. Lenin's.
11. Woodrow Wilson.

12. Aneurin Bevan.
13. Genghis Khan (1162–1227).
14. Lord Beaverbrook (William Maxwell Aitken).
15. President Tito.
16. Harold MacMillan.
17. Maria Estela Isabel Peron.
18. Margaret Grace Bondfield.
19. Daniel O'Connell.
20. Theodore Roosevelt.
21. Nelson Mandela and F W de Klerk.
22. Emmeline Pankhurst.
23. Haile Selassie.
24. Arthur Scargill.
25. David Ben Gurion.
26. Bismarck.
27. Vidkun Quisling.
28. Teacher and journalist.
29. Grigori Efimovich Rasputin (The Mad Monk) 1871–1916.
30. Stanley Baldwin.
31. William Pitt the Elder.
32. Mrs Bandaranaike.
33. Nancy Reagan.
34. Leon Trotsky.
35. Earl Mountbatten of Burma.
36. Eva Braun.
37. William McKinley (Mt McKinley is in Alaska).
38. El Cid.
39. Argentinian.
40. William Pitt the Younger.
41. Lady Donaldson.
42. Margaret Thatcher.

Films: Actors
1. Ernest Borgnine.
2. Jack Nicholson.
3. John Cleese.
4. Steve McQueen.
5. Charles Laughton.
6. Charlie Chaplin.
7. Peter Sellers.
8. Bob Hoskins.
9. Lou Costello.
10. James Coburn.
11. Audie Murphy.
12. Maurice Chevalier.

13. Peter Finch.
14. John Lennon.
15. Sylvester Stallone.
16. Anthony Hopkins.
17. Walter Pidgeon.
18. Rudolf Valentino.
19. James Cagney.
20. Oliver Hardy.
21. George Burns.
22. Robert Redford.
23. His thick horn-rimmed spectacles.
24. Al Jolson.
25. Johnny Cash.
26. Robert Shaw.
27. Humphrey Bogart.
28. Albert Finney.
29. Dustin Hoffman.
30. James Stewart.

Films: Actresses
1. Liza Minelli.
2. Ava Gardner.
3. Betty Grable.
4. Fay Wray.
5. Deborah Kerr.
6. *National Velvet*.
7. Genevieve Bujold.
8. Jodie Foster.
9. Greer Garson.
10. Jane Fonda.
11. Bo Derek.
12. Moira Shearer.
13. Mae West.
14. Marlene Dietrich.
15. Esther Williams.
16. Shirley Temple.
17. Shelley Winters.
18. Joan Crawford.
19. Greta Garbo.
20. Zsa Zsa Gabor.

Films: Books & Autobiographies
1. *The Great Gatsby*.
2. Peter Ustinov.

3. Shirley MacLaine.
4. Tony Curtis.
5. Marilyn Monroe's.
6. Bing Crosby's.
7. *Merry Christmas Mr Lawrence*.
8. The airborne attack on a series of bridges in Holland at Arnheim – a spearhead attack for allied troops into Germany.
9. Bob Hope's.
10. Eric Knight's.
11. Brooke Shields.
12. Ira Levin.
13. Dirk Bogarde.
14. Agatha Christie's.
15. Jack Warner's.

Films: Characters/Roles
1. *The Philadelphia Story*.
2. Clint Eastwood.
3. Henry Palmer.
4. Warren Beatty.
5. John Hurt and Richard Burton.
6. Philip Marlowe.
7. Johnny Weissmuller.
8. Michael Caine and Julie Walters.
9. Blofeld.
10. The Ringo Kid.
11. Robert Redford and Dustin Hoffman.
12. Gary Cooper.
13. Peter Sellers.
14. Catherine the Great.
15. Lex Luthor.
16. Sir Laurence Olivier.
17. Richard Gere.
18. They were child actors who were known as 'Our Gang'.
19. Harrison Ford.
20. Paul Newman.
21. Mel Gibson.
22. Richard Burton.
23. Robert Redford.
24. Al Pacino.
25. 007's boss in the *James Bond* books and films.
26. Alan Rickman.
27. *Star Wars*.
28. *The Lord of the Rings*. The characters are hobbits.

Films: Directors
1. Buster Keaton.
2. Milos Forman.
3. Alfred Hitchcock.
4. Burt Reynolds.
5. Orson Welles.
6. Billy Wilder.
7. Richard Attenborough (for the film *Gandhi*).
8. John Ford.
9. Robert Aldrich.
10. Cecil B De Mille.

Films: General
1. MGM.
2. *Fantasia*.
3. Ian Fleming wrote the film and created the character James Bond (alias 007).
4. *The Misfits*.
5. They were all concerned with the theme of insanity.
6. *The Incredible Journey*.
7. *On Golden Pond*.
8. They all concern boxing.
9. *Dr No* (1962); *From Russia With Love* (1963); *Goldfinger* (1964).
10. 1933.
11. Borstal.
12. The Mafia.
13. New York.
14. *Dr Jekyll and Mr Hyde*.
15. Scott Joplin's.
16. *Wild Geese II*.
17. All directed by Alfred Hitchcock.
18. *The Final Conflict*.
19. Hollywood.
20. *Carry on Sergeant*.
21. *Snow White and the Seven Dwarfs*.
22. *Running Brave*.
23. Ealing (London).
24. Pancake.
25. They were all directed by Steven Spielberg.
26. *The Shootist*.
27. *Gone With The Wind*.
28. *Never Say Never Again*.

Films: Musicals
1. André Previn.
2. *Cabaret.*
3. *The Jazz Singer.*
4. *The Duelling Cavalier.*
5. *Funny Girl.*
6. Bill Haley and the Comets.
7. *The Gay Divorcee.*
8. *A Hard Day's Night, Help, Yellow Submarine* and *Let It Be.*
9. *Love Me Tender.*
10. Paramount.
11. Audrey Hepburn.
12. *Mary Poppins.*
13. Cyd Charisse.
14. *Oliver!*
15. *The Wizard of Oz.*
16. Danny Kaye.
17. *Tommy.*
18. *Paint Your Wagon.* (The hit single was *Wandrin' Star*).
19. Ava Gardner.
20. *The Jungle Book.*
21. Jack Buchanan.
22. *The Sound Of Music.*

Films: Names & Nicknames
1. Marilyn Monroe.
2. Boris Karloff.
3. Charlie Chaplin.
4. Mary Pickford.
5. Rock Hudson.
6. Chico and Harpo.
7. Broncho Billy.
8. Roy Rogers.
9. John Wayne.
10. Jim Dougherty, Joe Di Maggio and Arthur Miller.

Food & Drink: Drinks
1. Cherries.
2. Mexico.
3. Bark of two South American trees.
4. From grain, potatoes or molasses and various spices.
5. Sugar cane.
6. Kabinett.

7. Spain.
8. From apples; originates in Normandy, N. France.
9. Coca-Cola.
10. Asti Spumante.
11. Chablis.
12. Madeira.
13. Robust.
14. Honey and water (and sometimes a little brandy).
15. Drambuie.
16. A very good quality cognac (been in the barrel for at least 5–8 years).
17. Ouzo.
18. Fino and oloroso.
19. Green or yellow.
20. Sake.
21. First made in Bourbon County (Kentucky).
22. Fish, particularly sturgeon (cleaned, dried swim-bladder).
23. A form of apricot brandy.
24. About 40 years.
25. They are types of sparkling wine.
26. Poteen.
27. Very dry.
28. Amontillado.
29. Vermouths, bitters and ainses.
30. Lindisfarne mead.
31. Bouquet.
32. Chianti.
33. Claret.
34. Aquavit.

Food & Drink: Name That Food
1. Baked Alaska.
2. Gorgonzola.
3. The tomato.
4. Truffles.
5. Tapioca.
6. Pikelets.
7. The apple.
8. Vitamin C.
9. Caramel.
10. A cauliflower cream soup.
11. Ghee.
12. Eccles cake.
13. Roquefort.
14. Frangipani.

15. Canapés.
16. A flitch.
17. Most: avocado. Least: cucumber.
18. Croutons.
19. Stilton.
20. Sloe.
21. Battenburg.
22. Hollandaise.
23. Cranberry.
24. Pecan.

Food & Drink: Traditional Dishes
1. Chapatti.
2. The Middle East. (Baked lamb stuffed with rice and nuts, flavoured with spices.)
3. Bubble and Squeak.
4. Tortilla.
5. Tunisia.
6. Dolmas.
7. Mulligatawny.
8. Cannelloni.
9. Mashed swede.
10. Dorset.
11. Guyana in South America.
12. Parmesan.
13. Yorkshire Parkin.
14. Pumpkin Pie.
15. Garibaldi.
16. Veal.
17. Chicory.
18. Simnel cake.
19. Scotland.
20. Espresso.

Food & Drink: What Is It?
1. Bouquet garni.
2. Cocotte.
3. Julienne.
4. It describes pasta that is cooked and feels firm to the teeth when it is bitten.
5. A clear thin broth obtained by boiling meat or beef bones in seasoned water.
6. Fruit preserved or stewed in syrup.
7. Florentine.

8. Walnuts.
9. A German black bread made with coarse rye flour.
10. Pasta shapes.
11. Kiwi fruit.
12. Small round dumplings made of potatoes, flour or semolina.
13. Sliced or shredded raw vegetables.
14. Swiss chard.
15. Cabbage.
16. A famous Spanish soup, usually served cold.
17. Small French cakes or biscuits.
18. The film which forms on the sides of a bottle of good old port (which resembles the wings of bees).
19. A German dish of pickled cabbage.
20. Shark.
21. The edible entrails of a deer or other animal.
22. A type of gelatine, made from seaweed.

Games & Pastimes
1. Seven.
2. The Queen of Spades.
3. 37.
4. When he castles (moving a castle (rook) and a King together).
5. Telling fortunes.
6. Diabolo.
7. 50.
8. 15.
9. B H L E F T. (Each letter being an initial of a part of a beetle).
10. Maj-jong.
11. Pelota.
12. Henry VII and Henry VIII.
13. Chicane.
14. Skipping a flat stone over the surface of calm water.
15. Pontoon.
16. 28.
17. Dice.
18. Candlestick; dagger; lead piping; revolver; rope; spanner.
19. Eight.
20. Twelve.
21. The Rubic Cube
22. Dice.
23. In a straight line, vertically or horizontally.
24. 108 cards (two regular packs and four jokers).
25. 13.
26. 144.
27. In a pack of tarot cards.

28. Turkey.
29. Bagatelle.
30. Nine of Diamonds (resembles the armour of Lord Stair who shared in sanctioning the Massacre of Glencoe in 1692).
31. Macrame.
32. 64.

General Knowledge

1. France.
2. Inner Temple, Middle Temple, Lincoln's Inn and Gray's Inn.
3. Six.
4. The Red Cross.
5. Table.
6. 32.
7. Eastern, Central, Mountain and Pacific.
8. In recognition for outstanding services to ballet.
9. Bournville.
10. Toby.
11. Freemasons.
12. Morganatic marriage.
13. Terracotta.
14. *The Ladies Mercury*.
15. Sheepdog trials.
16. Jet.
17. 9 carat.
18. Red, orange, yellow, green, blue, indigo and violet.
19. Ferris Wheel.
20. English Tourist Board.
21. 24.
22. Fair Isle.
23. Journalism, literature and music.
24. Balsa wood.
25. Big Top.
26. Licensed to kill.
27. 1050.
28. Your Grace.
29. French polish.
30. Belgium; France; West Germany; Italy; Luxembourg; The Netherlands.
31. Four.
32. Every ten years.
33. Picadors.
34. Items from seashells and bone and ivory.
35. Perspex.
36. Willow Pattern.

37. Drug addiction.
38. Their height – they are the world's tallest people.
39. The Sorbonne (Paris).
40. Sheep bend, sheep shank, clove hitch, round turn, two and a half hitches, bowline knot.
41. 80.
42. A millenium.
43. Gingerbread.
44. 1971.
45. *x*.
46. In Scottish courts.
47. M.
48. Harvard.
49. Bossa Nova.
50. Lutine Bell.
51. Scotland Yard.
52. 10.
53. Ruskin College, Oxford.
54. A person must not build a wall which would stop daylight entering another person's building.
55. 3.
56. A tree (thought to be 3–4,000 years old).
57. Queen's Badge.
58. 360.
59. 1,500 miles.
60. Donald McGill.
61. 180.
62. The widowed and their children.
63. Town mark, maker's mark, date letter and sterling letter.
64. Tent stitch.
65. Conga.
66. Columbine.
67. *The Nautical Almanac*.
68. Church affairs.
69. Ebony.
70. Finnish.
71. In a library.

Geographical Terms
1. Tropic of Cancer.
2. A drowned river valley.
3. Anti-cyclone.
4. The degree of Longitude passing through Greenwich, i.e. 0°.
5. Sirocco.
6. Seismology.

258

7. 90°N.
8. Meteorology.
9. A rock which has been restructured by heat or pressure.
10. Geysers.
11. Antarctic Circle.
12. A smooth hill shaped by moving ice made up of glacial drift or till.
13. They are all New Towns.
14. Altitude.
15. 12.
16. West coast of the USA, centred on San Francisco.
17. Tundra.
18. Arête.
19. A cold wind that blows down the Rhone Valley in France.
20. Lava.
21. Waterspout.
22. Cataract.

Geography: Islands
1. Vancouver Island.
2. Leeward Islands.
3. Tobermory.
4. The Balearic Islands.
5. Sark.
6. The Azores.
7. Indian Ocean.
8. Borneo, Madagascar and Sumatra.
9. Ellis Island.
10. Greenland (Australia being a continental land mass).
11. Zanzibar.
12. Anglesey.
13. Crete.
14. Corsica.
15. Sri Lanka.
16. The Friendly Islands.
17. Italy.
18. Falkland Islands.
19. Channel Islands.
20. Barbados.
21. Tierra del Fuego.
22. The Bermudas.
23. North Island (New Zealand).
24. Tahiti.
25. Gozo.
26. Orkney, North Scotland.

27. Bryher, St Agnes, St Martin's, St Mary's, Tresco.
28. Malta.
29. Lindisfarne.
30. Borneo.
31. Aran Islands.
32. Skye.
33. Canary Islands.
34. A chain of volcanic islands in the North Pacific.
35. Faroe Islands.
36. Shetland Islands.
37. Greece.
38. Anglesey, North Wales.
39. Madagascar.
40. Sumatra.
41. The Island of Staffa in the Inner Hebrides.
42. In the Southern Indian Ocean.
43. Cuba.
44. Bishop Rock.
45. Cayman Islands.
46. Easter Island.
47. They are a small chain of islands south of Florida.
48. Jersey.

Geography: Mountains & Volcanoes
 1. Argentina.
 2. Mount McKinley, Alaska.
 3. South Africa (also partly in Swaziland and Lesotho).
 4. Vesuvius.
 5. The Cheviot Hills.
 6. The Andes.
 7. Khyber Pass.
 8. Australia.
 9. Valley of Ten Thousand Smokes.
10. Snowdon, in Wales.
11. Canada.
12. Exmoor.
13. Mount Etna.
14. Fujiyama.
15. Northern Ireland.
16. Kilimanjaro.
17. Mexico.
18. K2 (in the Karakoram Range between India and China).
19. Dolomites (Italy).
20. Appalachian Mountains (N America).
21. Andes.

22. New Zealand.
23. Mount Everest.
24. Greece.
25. Pyrenees.
26. Central Australia, near Alice Springs.
27. County Kerry, SW Ireland.
28. Table Mountain.
29. Mont Blanc.
30. Apennines.
31. They are all active volcanoes.
32. Adirondack Mountains.

Geography: Regions, Countries & States
1. Angola.
2. California.
3. Tasmania.
4. Death Valley, California.
5. South West Africa.
6. Equador.
7. Brasilia.
8. In Romania.
9. Quebec (largest); Prince Edward Island (smallest).
10. Liberia.
11. Algarve.
12. Antarctica.
13. The Vatican.
14. Scotland.
15. Paraguay.
16. Tennessee.
17. Malawi.
18. Malin Head, Donegal.
19. New York.
20. Canada.
21. Scotland.
22. Belgium.
23. Taiwan.
24. Kent.
25. Venezuela (after Venice).
26. Bangladesh.
27. The Borders.
28. Norway.
29. France.
30. Texas.
31. Belize.
32. The Naze.

33. Saudi Arabia.
34. Thailand.
35. Pampas.
36. Belgium, The Netherlands and Luxembourg.
37. Arizona.
38. Spain.
39. Gwent.
40. Fray Bentos.
41. Andorra.
42. Serengeti.
43. Toledo.
44. Ireland.
45. The Trossachs.
46. Newfoundland, Canada.

Geography: Towns & Cities
1. Syria.
2. Washington (USA).
3. Cumbernauld.
4. Djakarta.
5. Pakistan.
6. Charleston.
7. Port Said.
8. Lerwick in the Shetlands.
9. Khartoum.
10. Constantinople and Byzantium.
11. Tallahasse.
12. Duisburg, Germany.
13. New York.
14. Kabul.
15. Toronto, Canada.
16. Syracuse.
17. Arizona.
18. Ebbw Vale.
19. Monte Carlo.
20. New Hampshire.
21. Belfast.
22. Santiago.
23. Rome.
24. Montevideo.
25. Appleby.
26. New York.
27. Belgium.
28. Reykjavik.
29. Dublin.

30. Arbroath.
31. Cornwall.
32. Rio de Janeiro.
33. Quebec.
34. Montreal.
35. Palermo.
36. Burma.
37. Denver.
38. Boston.
39. Rome.
40. Paraguay.
41. Cologne.
42. Fort Lauderdale.
43. Albany.
44. Hamilton.
45. Havana.
46. Nassau.
47. Darwin.
48. Lossiemouth.
49. Ottawa.
50. Alexandria.
51. Athens.
52. Copenhagen.
53. Cirencester.
54. Manila.
55. Berlin.
56. Dar es Salaam.
57. Rabat.
58. Christchurch (on South Island).
59. Inverness.
60. New York.

Geography: Waters & Waterways
1. Northern Australia.
2. Germany – in the Black Forest.
3. Suez Canal.
4. Lake Garda.
5. The Rio Grande.
6. New Orleans.
7. The Straits of Magellan.
8. Caledonian Canal.
9. River Tiber.
10. The Panama Canal.
11. Lake Superior.
12. River Severn.

13. Irish Sea.
14. Caspian Sea.
15. Cook Strait.
16. Sounds.
17. The Solent.
18. Nile, Amazon, Mississippi and Yangtze.
19. River Jordan.
20. River Thames.
21. They all lie below sea level.
22. Lake Erie and Lake Ontario.
23. Old Faithful.
24. Hudson Bay.
25. Archipelago.
26. London and Birmingham
27. Lake Michigan.
28. Wadi.
29. Little Minch.
30. The Nile.
31. Indian Ocean.
32. River Seine.
33. South China Sea.
34. The Bosporus.
35. River Scheldt.
36. Solway Firth.
37. New Zealand.
38. The Loire.
39. The Rivers Tigris and Euphrates.
40. Caspian Sea.
41. Dardanelles. (Its ancient name was Hellespont.)
42. Niagara Falls.
43. The North West Passage.
44. Lake Como.
45. The Arctic.
46. The straits of Messina.
47. Po.
48. Hungary.
49. The Skagerrak.
50. The Danube.
51. The Pool of London.
52. Venezuela (Angel Falls).
53. The Baltic Sea.
54. The St Lawrence.
55. Lake Titicaca.
56. The River Shannon in Eire.
57. Billabong.
58. The Glomma.

59. Dogger Bank.
60. The Norfolk Broads.

Great Britain
1. Melton Mowbray.
2. The House of Commons is still sitting.
3. South Shields.
4. Edinburgh.
5. Manchester.
6. Lizard Point, Cornwall.
7. The Eddystone Lighthouse.
8. Telford. (Thomas Telford.)
9. Salop.
10. Woolsack.
11. Whipsnade.
12. Portsmouth.
13. Blackpool.
14. Grasmere.
15. The Backs.
16. Gretna Green.
17. York.
18. Richmond Park.
19. Alton Towers.
20. 250 miles.
21. Winchester School.
22. Charles II (who escaped from his enemies by hiding in a tree).
23. Chester.
24. They are all highways constructed by the Romans.
25. Perth.
26. Llantrisant, Mid Glamorgan, Wales.
27. Bamburgh, Northumberland.
28. Brighton.
29. Australia.
30. March.
31. The Potteries.
32. Aldermaston.
33. Pembrokeshire.
34. Cowes.
35. Cheltenham.
36. Holyrood House.
37. Cambridge.
38. Devon.
39. Lytham St Annes, Lancashire.
40. Shetland Islands.
41. Royal National Lifeboat Institution.

42. Bristol.
43. Birmingham.
44. Brecon Beacons.
45. 73 miles long from Solway Firth to Wallsend on Tyne.
46. Queen's House, Tower of London.
47. The Bodleian Library.
48. Porters at Billingsgate Fish Market.
49. Basildon.
50. Welsh.
51. Parkhurst.
52. Trinity House Corporation.
53. Victoria Tower.

History: Ancient – Mediaeval
1. Hannibal.
2. Matilda.
3. Ermine Street.
4. Caractacus or Caradoc.
5. The Bastille.
6. Oxford (founded 1167).
7. Caledonia.
8. Attila.
9. Lamprey.
10. Aztec Empire in Mexico.
11. An earthwork built by Offa, King of Mercia, to divide Wales from the Anglo-Saxons.
12. Richard (I) the Lionheart.
13. Spartacus.
14. Merchants.
15. Emperor Constantine.
16. He had a survey carried out (the Domesday Book).
17. The Unready.
18. He led the first Crusade.
19. Alexander the Great.
20. Nero.
21. Robert the Bruce, King of Scots.
22. Nebuchadnezzar.
23. Eton College.
24. Westminster Abbey.
25. Colchester and St Albans.
26. The wheel.
27. Alfred (the Great).
28. Belgians.
29. The Iceni.
30. He was a minstrel.

31. King Harold at the Battle of Hastings.
32. Charlemagne.
33. It, like Pompeii, was destroyed when Vesuvius erupted.
34. William I – the Conqueror.
35. Brian Boru.
36. Carthage.
37. 116 years (1337–1453).
38. The Mediterranean.
39. A tax to raise money to resist the Danish invasion.
40. The Battle of Crecy.
41. Canute.
42. The Magna Carta.
43. Ming.
44. The Persian Empire.
45. Launching missiles or stones – it was a seige engine.
46. Edward II.
47. Peterhouse.

History: 16th – 18th Centuries

1. Cardinal Wolsey.
2. Mary, Queen of Scots.
3. Jacobites.
4. Coldstream Guards.
5. James II.
6. For the war between the American colonies and British rulers to begin.
7. Imprisonment without trial.
8. The War of Austrian Succession.
9. Lord Protector.
10. Four days.
11. James Stuart (his father).
12. Queen Anne.
13. Tumbrels or Tumbrils.
14. Battle of Culloden.
15. Abraham Lincoln.
16. Nell Gwyn.
17. Britain, the Netherlands and Spain.
18. Public executions.
19. Pirates.
20. 4th July 1776.
21. Field of the Cloth of Gold.
22. A unicorn.
23. Walter Raleigh.
24. Edward VI, Mary I and Elizabeth I.
25. Sansculottes.

26. *The Ark*.
27. Manhattan Island.
28. Bridgewater Canal.
29. Sir Walter Raleigh.
30. *Pelican*.
31. Cavaliers.
32. The Seven Years War.
33. The Black Death.
34. Delaware; Pennsylvania; New Jersey; Georgia; Connecticut.
35. Fotheringay Castle.
36. He committed suicide.
37. Sir Richard Arkwright.
38. Pitcairn.
39. Philip II.
40. Sedgemoor.
41. 17th Century (1630–50).
42. King Charles II.
43. They were both pretenders to the English throne.
44. 'Butcher'.
45. South Africa – they were Boers who trekked from Transvaal to the Orange Free State.

History: 19th – 20th Centuries
1. Battle of Trafalgar.
2. *General Belgrano*.
3. The Tomb of Tutankhamun.
4. The Chartists.
5. Ireland, 1916.
6. *The Hindenberg*.
7. The Nuremberg Trials.
8. Spencer Perceval.
9. Prince Albert (Queen Victoria's husband).
10. 1936–39.
11. Hastings Banda.
12. Railway steam engines. The Rocket won.
13. The Molly Maguires.
14. The Boers and the Zulus.
15. Archduke Ferdinand's at Sarajevo.
16. Tolpuddle Martyrs.
17. A body of spies behind a fighting front.
18. Spain.
19. A raft in the middle of a river.
20. Singapore.
21. Liberia or Ethiopia.
22. International Monetary Fund.

23. The potato famine in Ireland, 1847.
24. Mau-Mau.
25. The New Deal.
26. Geneva Convention.
27. The consumption and sale of alcoholic drinks.
28. Louis Mountbatten, 1st Earl of Burma. 1947.
29. Fidel Castro.
30. Corsica.
31. Hiroshima and Nagasaki.
32. Montreal, Canada.
33. Cyprus.
34. Austrian.
35. Plassey.
36. H M Stanley and Dr Livingstone met.
37. First Lord of the Admiralty.
38. The Luddites.
39. Those taking part in the gold rush in California in 1849.
40. Abyssinia.
41. Duke of Wellington.
42. The *Titanic* sank.
43. The Combination Acts.
44. Albania.
45. The Cat and Mouse Act.
46. A landslide disaster killed 144 children.
47. The Treaty of Versailles.

Inventions
1. A safety lamp for miners.
2. The Hovercraft.
3. Hot air balloon.
4. 1797.
5. Carpet sweeper.
6. *Locomotion No. 1*.
7. Photography.
8. Dynamite.
9. The zip fastener.
10. The typewriter.
11. Signalling (sending morse messages).
12. 1815.
13. The safety pin.
14. 'Mary had a little lamb.'
15. The cinema.
16. Television.
17. The mechanical lift.
18. The washing machine.

19. Colt.
20. Traffic lights.
21. The Skyscraper.
22. Torpedo.
23. Sonar.
24. Belfast.

Inventors
1. John Walker.
2. Guglielmo Marconi (in 1901).
3. George Eastman.
4. Thomas Alva Edison.
5. Benjamin Franklin.
6. Sir Barnes Nevis Wallis.
7. Samuel Crompton.
8. Gabriel Fahrenheit.
9. Frank Whittle.
10. Robert Herries.
11. Cecil Booth.
12. Clarence Birdseye.
13. Jacques Cousteau.
14. Professor Roentgen (or Röntgen).
15. Henry Maudslay.
16. Lasalo Biro.
17. Archimedes.
18. James Nielson.
19. Charles Goodyear.
20. Karl Benz.
21. Edward Teller.
22. William Caxton.
23. Sir David Brewster.
24. Orville and Wilbur Wright.
25. Sir Isaac Pitman.
26. Samuel Morse.

Language
1. Au fait.
2. Blueberries.
3. Book.
4. Let the buyer beware.
5. To God (or Go with God).
6. Condominium.
7. A midwife.
8. La Manche.

9. Delta.
10. Out of order/course (hence, extra dish).
11. I think – therefore I am.
12. Candy.
13. 40.
14. Peace.
15. Puttees.
16. A kilt.
17. Good Health.
18. Sayonara.
19. Of sound mind – sane.
20. Polder.
21. I've found it.
22. Occidental.
23. Gringos.
24. Welcome.
25. Hacienda.
26. Spoonerism.
27. Autobahn.
28. A faucet.
29. Breton.
30. Carabiniere.
31. Long live Ireland.
32. Gravedigger.
33. Verbatim.
34. Attorney.
35. Thanks be to God.
36. Six.
37. El Dorado.
38. Déjà vû.
39. O Come All Ye Faithful.
40. Guerilla.
41. Façade.
42. Checkers.

Literary Characters
1. Scarlet Pimpernel.
2. Don Quixote.
3. Lewis Eliot.
4. Father Brown.
5. Hercule Poirot.
6. Don Juan.
7. Winston Smith.
8. Flopsy, Mopsy, Cotton-tail and Peter.
9. Kimball O'Hara.

10. Ben Gunn.
11. Winnie The Pooh.
12. Rip Van Winkle.
13. Queen of Hearts.
14. Fagin.
15. Village carpenter.
16. Detective Superintendent Maigret.
17. A tiger.
18. Yahoo.
19. Barkis.
20. The pigs.
21. Captain Nemo.
22. The Cheshire cat.
23. Rabbits.
24. Athos.
25. Billy Bunter.
26. Paddington Bear.
27. An otter.
28. Count Dracula.
29. Joe Lampton.
30. Modesty Blaise.
31. Lemuel Gulliver.
32. Ichabod Crane.
33. Uncle Remus.
34. Walter Mitty.
35. Frankenstein.
36. Dr Finlay.
37. Dr Doolittle.

Literature: Authors
 1. Lewis Carroll.
 2. Samuel Pepys.
 3. Arthur Ransome.
 4. Aesop's.
 5. Voltaire.
 6. James Herriot.
 7. John Le Carre.
 8. Charles Dickens.
 9. Alexander Solzhenitsyn.
10. George Orwell.
11. Sir James Matthew Barrie.
12. William Wilkie Colins.
13. Nina Bawden.
14. Mark Twain.

Literature: Book Titles

1. *Mein Kampf.*
2. *The Brotherhood.*
3. *Moby Dick.*
4. *The Forsyte Saga.*
5. *The Origin of Species.*
6. *1984.*
7. *Little Women.*
8. *War and Peace.*
9. *A Clockwork Orange.*
10. *Tom Jones.*
11. *Gone With The Wind.*
12. *First Impressions.*
13. *Rebecca.*
14. *Great Expectations.*
15. *Jude The Obscure.*
16. *Shirley.*
17. *A Portrait of The Artist As A Young Man.*
18. *She Stoops To Conquer.*
19. *Savrola.*
20. *Brighton Rock.*
21. *The Time Machine.*
22. *Catch 22.*
23. *The Good Companions.*
24. *Vanity Fair.*
25. *The Mystery of Edwin Drood.*
26. *Uncle Tom's Cabin.*
27. *The Just So Stories.*
28. *The Lord Of The Rings.*
29. *White Fang.*
30. *Middlemarch.*
31. *Lord Of The Flies.*
32. *Burke's Peerage.*
33. *Lady Chatterley's Lover.*
34. *Love On The Dole.*
35. *The Weir Of Hermiston.*
36. *All Quiet On The Western Front.*

Literature: Children's Books

1. Tom.
2. Flicka.
3. Nancy Drew.
4. *The Moomins.*
5. *Black Pig.*

6. Roberta (Bobby), Peter and Phyllis.
7. Black Beauty.
8. *Just William* (and sequels).
9. Larry the Lamb and Dennis the Dachshund.
10. Gosling (goose).
11. Bastable.
12. Tyneside (South Shields).
13. She was thrown from a defective swing which she'd been forbidden to use.
14. Boggis, Bunce and Bean.
15. Lord Bertie Lissie.
16. Jones The Steam.
17. He sees visions of the future.
18. Little Red Fox.
19. Mowgli.
20. Ermintrude.
21. Miss Eglantine Price.
22. Thomas.
23. George.
24. Bertie.
25. Hardy.
26. *The Tales of Beatrix Potter*.
27. In the *Winnie The Pooh* stories.
28. Susan, Peter, Edmund and Lucy Pevensie.
29. Teddy and Looby Loo.
30. Long John Silver.
31. Almanzo Wilder.
32. Darling.
33. Toad of Toad Hall.
34. Meg, Jo, Beth and Amy.
35. Marmalade sandwiches.
36. The Mister Men.
37. Celeste.
38. Millicent Margaret Amanda.
39. Lord Fauntleroy.
40. Heidi.

Literature: General
1. Travel guides.
2. Angling (*Complete Angler*, 1653).
3. La Mancha.
4. Tuberculosis.
5. Branwell.
6. California.
7. Dylan Thomas (*Under Milk Wood*).

8. Angry Young Men.
9. E H Shepard.
10. 221B Baker Street.
11. Broadstairs, Kent.
12. E.
13. A stammer.
14. By drowning.
15. Five.
16. Exmoor.
17. Shakespeare.
18. 173 novels.
19. Joseph Pulitzer.
20. Big game hunting.
21. Heaven.
22. Allegory.
23. Lytton Strachey.
24. It is a manuscript of the four gospels.
25. John Debrett.
26. Scheherazade.
27. Charles Dickens.
28. Architect.
29. Phiz.
30. South Africa.
31. Ghosting.
32. William Shakespeare.

Literature: Poets & Poetry

1. Geoffrey Chaucer.
2. William Blake.
3. Philip Larkin.
4. Arthur Henry Hallam.
5. Derby and Joan.
6. C Day Lewis.
7. W B Yeats.
8. A E Housman.
9. Tennyson (*The Charge of The Light Brigade*).
10. Andrew Marvell.
11. *The Daffodils* (Wordsworth).
12. Belinda.
13. Sylvia Plath.
14. Sir Walter Scott.
15. T S Elliot.
16. Edgar Allan Poe.
17. A A Milne.
18. John Keats.

19. Albatross.
20. Robert Burns.
21. Edward Lear.
22. William Cowper.
23. Louis MacNeice.
24. William Wordsworth.
25. Wordsworth, Coleridge and Southey.
26. Henry, McGough and Patten.
27. John Taylor.
28. Robert Browning.
29. To the north of Katmandu.
30. James Hogg.
31. Xanadu.
32. Shelley.
33. Rats (*The Pied Piper of Hamelin*).
34. Walter de la Mare.
35. A E.
36. Rupert Brooke.
37. The Cuckoo.
38. To a mouse.

Literature: Shakespeare
1. Banquo.
2. Oberon.
3. Hamlet.
4. Falstaff.
5. *The Tempest*.
6. *Twelfth Night*.
7. *As You Like It*.
8. Calphurnia (Caesar's); Portia (Brutus's).
9. Richard III.
10. *The Winter's Tale*.
11. *King Lear* and *Othello*.
12. Agincourt.
13. *All's Well That Ends Well*.
14. Jacques (*As You Like It*).
15. Octavia.
16. A character named Ariel.
17. Cordelia.
18. Iago.
19. *Macbeth*.
20. *A Midsummer Night's Dream*.
21. Tyre.
22. Robin Goodfellow.
23. *All's Well That End's Well*.

276

24. *Hamlet, Prince of Denmark.*
25. Sebastian.
26. Shylock.
27. Husband and wife.
28. Katherina.
29. *Romeo and Juliet.*
30. She committed suicide by drowning.
31. Touchstone.
32. Brabantio.
33. *The Tempest.*
34. Jessica.
35. King of Britain.

Literature: Who Wrote?
1. Hans Christian Andersen.
2. Jerome K Jerome.
3. James Hilton.
4. Sir Ernest Henry Shackleton.
5. John Fowles.
6. John Ford.
7. Samuel Butler.
8. Dostoyevsky.
9. Flora Thompson.
10. Edith Nesbit.
11. James Joyce.
12. Sidney Sheldon.
13. Simone de Beauvoir.
14. John Le Carré.
15. John Knox.
16. William Faulkner.
17. Evelyn Waugh.
18. Elizabeth Gaskell.
19. Laurence Sterne.
20. Joseph Conrad.
21. Raymond Briggs.
22. James Fenimore Cooper.
23. Judith Krantz.
24. Arnold Bennett.
25. Germaine Greer.
26. Oscar Wilde.
27. Susan Howatch.
28. Frederick Forsyth.
29. John Wyndham.
30. Alexandre Dumas.
31. Isabella Mary Beeton.

32. Dorothy L Sayers.
33. Vera Brittain.
34. Elspeth Huxley.
35. Walter De La Mare.
36. Thomas Hughes.
37. A A Milne.
38. Virginia Woolf.
39. Washington Irving.
40. H E Bates.
41. Tobias Smollett.
42. Jules Verne.
43. Jack London.
44. Edward Gibbon.
45. Anita Loos.
46. Muriel Spark.
47. Henry James.
48. Maria Edgeworth.
49. Thomas Hardy.
50. Sir Winston Churchill.
51. Graham Greene.
52. Brendan Behan.
53. Jeffrey Archer.
54. H G Wells.
55. Frederick Marryat.
56. P D James.
57. John Milton.
58. Herman Melville.
59. Alison Uttley.
60. Lewis Caroll.

London
1. The Houses of Parliament.
2. Circle Line.
3. The dome of St Paul's Cathedral.
4. Lambeth.
5. Downing Street.
6. Tavistock Square.
7. Paxton and Whitfield.
8. Southend-on-Sea.
9. Manette Street (Dr Manette).
10. Smithfield.
11. Kensal Green Cemetery (North Kensington).
12. St Giles High Street.
13. In Hyde Park – an area which is popular with horse riders.
14. Piccadilly Circus.

278

15. The House of Lords.
16. Oxford Street.
17. The Tube.
18. Harley Street.
19. The Bank of England.
20. Mermaid Tavern.
21. Trinity Square Gardens.
22. St Martin-in-the-fields.
23. Old Bailey.
24. To commemorate the capture of Porto Bello (Gulf of Mexico), 1739.
25. The Inner Temple Gateway. (Son of James I.)
26. Little America (as the American Embassy is sited here).
27. Carnaby Street.
28. Wardour Street.
29. After Sir Hans Sloane, a distinguished physician.

Mathematics
1. Trigonometry.
2. Nought and one.
3. A tangent.
4. Seventy.
5. Infinity.
6. Twelve.
7. Twenty past nine.
8. They are all prime numbers.
9. John Napier.
10. Hexagonal.
11. 3.142.
12. Converting °Fahrenheit to °Centigrade.

Medical Matters: General
1. Thermometer.
2. The throat.
3. Gynaecology.
4. Physiotherapy.
5. Whether or not you are colour-blind.
6. The study and treatment of skin diseases.
7. *The Lancet*.
8. Phrenology.
9. Acupuncture.
10. Deadly Nightshade.
11. Paediatrics.
12. Neurology.

13. Freckles.
14. A local anaesthetic.
15. The Hippocratic Oath.
16. The circulation of the blood.
17. Compound fracture.
18. Hysterectomy.
19. Nigeria.
20. Physiology.
21. First man to receive a human heart transplant and survive.
22. Quinine.

Medical Matters: The Human Body
1. 37°C.
2. Incisors, canine, pre-molars and molars.
3. Three pounds.
4. 46.
5. The soft area of cartilage on a baby's head where the skull bones have not yet joined.
6. Epidermis and dermis.
7. A, B, AB and O.
8. The breast bone.
9. The navel or 'belly button'.
10. Insulin.
11. The nose.
12. In the hand.
13. The diaphragm.
14. In the ear.
15. In the throat.
16. Humerus, radius and ulna.
17. 70–74.
18. 12.
19. The femur (thigh bone).
20. The knee-cap.
21. 206.
22. 32.
23. Bile.
24. Veins.
25. In the heart and lungs.
26. Shoulder blade.
27. Serum.
28. In the neck.
29. Ligament.
30. In the feet.
31. 22.

32. The iris.
33. Upper jaw (maxilla) and lower jaw (mandible).

Medical Matters: Medical Conditions

1. You would be bald.
2. Indigestion.
3. The kidney.
4. The liver.
5. Bubonic Plague.
6. Lumbago.
7. Cataract.
8. Anaemia.
9. Seasickness.
10. Scurvy.
11. Legionnaires Disease.
12. The kidneys.
13. Anorexia Nervosa.
14. Hands and feet.
15. Siamese Twins.
16. Vitamin D.
17. Malaria.
18. Dyslexia.
19. Tsetse fly.
20. An artificial limb.
21. Eyes.
22. In old age.
23. Red and green.
24. Whooping Cough.
25. Chickenpox.
26. Rubella.
27. Pyorrhoea.
28. Eyes.
29. Mumps.
30. Lock-jaw.
31. Nose-bleed.
32. Hypochondriac.
33. Amnesia.
34. The brain.
35. Down's Syndrome.
36. Bad breath.
37. Eyes (inflammation of the eye).
38. Kleptomania.
39. Blood poisoning.
40. Bedwetting.

Money

1. Sovereign.
2. 1971.
3. One Groat.
4. Bureau de change.
5. Ten.
6. From the checkered tablecloth on which accounts were calculated in early Norman times.
7. International Monetary Fund.
8. 252.
9. Bear.
10. Dow Jones Index.
11. Nine linked hands circled around the perimeter.
12. The Gnomes of Zurich.
13. Copper and nickel (or cupro-nickel).
14. Gross National Product.
15. The Bourse.
16. The twelve-sided threepenny piece.
17. The shilling.

Mottoes

1. Royal National Lifeboat Institution.
2. The Prince of Wales.
3. 'The Mounties always get their man.'
4. John Lewis.
5. Royal Air Force.
6. 'Who Dares, Wins.'
7. 'Fidelity, Bravery, Integrity.'
8. 'Liberty, Equality, Fraternity.'
9. The Salvation Army.
10. 'All for one, one for all.'

Music: Composers

1. Stravinsky.
2. Duke Ellington.
3. Bach.
4. Handel.
5. Nine.
6. Ignace Jan Paderewski.
7. Englebert Humperdinck.
8. Brahms.
9. Delius.
10. Greig.

11. Liszt.
12. Debussy.
13. Berlioz.
14. Noel Coward.
15. Bernstein.
16. Dvorak.
17. Simon and Garfunkel.
18. Baroque.
19. The British National Anthem.
20. Elgar.
21. Hungarian.
22. Gershwin.
23. Chopin.
24. Shostakovich.
25. Jean Baptiste Lully.
26. Irving Berlin.
27. Tchaikovsky.
28. Beethoven.
29. Mussorgsky.
30. Jerome Kern.
31. Handel.
32. Sir Arthur Sullivan.
33. John Philip Sousa.
34. Prokofiev.
35. Rogers and Hammerstein.
36. Holst.

Music: General
1. 'Clock' Symphony.
2. Leonard Bernstein.
3. Louis Armstrong.
4. Cliff Richard.
5. Malvern Festival.
6. Sir Henry Joseph Wood.
7. *Guys and Dolls*.
8. The Cavern.
9. Elvis Presley.
10. La Marseillaise.
11. *Moonlight Serenade*.
12. Charleston.
13. *Love Me Do*.
14. Fats Domino.
15. *The Nutcracker Suite*.
16. Waltz.
17. *Christmas Symphony*.

18. Albert Schweitzer.
19. Satchmo.
20. Connie Francis.
21. Nashville.
22. Bob Dylan.
23. *Choral Symphony*.
24. Jenny Lind.
25. American.
26. Count Basie.

Music: Instruments
1. Tuba.
2. Four.
3. Piano.
4. Bagpipes.
5. Castanets.
6. Strings, woodwind, brass and percussion.
7. Clarinet.
8. Antonio Stradivari.
9. Baby grand.
10. Violoncello.
11. Harmonica (mouth organ).
12. Balalaika.
13. Lyre.
14. Cornet.
15. Trumpet, trombone, horn and tuba.
16. Cello.
17. Trombone.
18. Double Bass.
19. Woodwind.
20. 88 (52 white, 36 black).
21. Trumpet.
22. Flute.
23. Euphonium.
24. Violin.
25. Guitar.
26. Pablo Casals.

Music: Opera
1. Puccini.
2. *Carmen*.
3. Benjamin Britten's.
4. Kathleen Ferrier.
5. The Barber of Seville.

284

6. *Fidelio*.
7. Edith Mary Coates.
8. Prokofiev.
9. Bartók.
10. *Porgy and Bess*.
11. William Tell.
12. The Coronation of Queen Elizabeth II.
13. Engelbert Humperdinck.
14. Wagner.
15. Puccini.
16. Mozart. 'Thus so all women.'
17. Bizet.
18. Mussorgsky.
19. Australian.
20. Milan.
21. *The Magic Flute*.

Musical Terms
1. Repeat from beginning.
2. Gondoliers.
3. Overture.
4. A Cappella.
5. Soprano or Treble, Alto, Tenor, Bass.
6. Quickly or lively.
7. Very loud (loudest).
8. A small machine used to mark time at a steady beat.
9. Alto.
10. Slow.
11. Aria.
12. Baritone.
13. Baton.
14. The playing, by plucking with the fingers, of an instrument which is normally played with a bow.
15. Contralto.
16. Barber-shop quartet.
17. Tin Pan Alley.

Mythology: Greek & Roman
1. Apollo.
2. He ran the first marathon.
3. Paris fired an arrow (guided by Apollo) into his heel.
4. Romulus and Remus.
5. Adonis.
6. Artemis.

7. Hera.
8. Prometheus.
9. Peace.
10. Menelaus.
11. Helicon.
12. Icarus.
13. Pan.
14. Ceres.
15. The Gorgons.
16. Troilus.
17. Orpheus.
18. Aurora.
19. Fleetness of foot.
20. The peacock (on to his tail).
21. Saturday (after Saturn).
22. Ulysses.
23. Ariadne.
24. Ares.
25. Poseidon.
26. Boar.
27. *Argo*.
28. Jupiter.
29. Ajax.
30. Pegasus.
31. Vulcan.
32. Daphne.
33. Nike.
34. Cyclops.
35. Narcissus.
36. Cassandra.
37. Janus (gave name to January).
38. A single horse hair.
39. Mercury.
40. Atlas.
41. Pygmalion.
42. Somnus (somnolent).

Mythology: Other Myths and Legends
1. A dragon.
2. Tintagel.
3. King Cole.
4. Sherwood Forest.
5. A griffin.
6. A jackal.
7. Mermaid.

286

8. *The Flying Dutchman*.
9. He crossed a running stream.
10. Lady Godiva.
11. King Midas.
12. Ra.
13. Scandinavian.
14. The cup from which Christ drank at the last supper.
15. Beowulf.
16. The gift of the gab.
17. Joan.
18. The River Rhine.
19. A creature which is half seal, half man.
20. Sir Mordred.
21. Peeping Tom.
22. Valhalla.
23. Allan-a-Dale.
24. Chrysanthemum.
25. 150.
26. Legendary giants (associated with the City of London).
27. Black Bess.
28. Chukwa.

Names: People
1. John Montagu.
2. Burke.
3. Uncle Sam.
4. Tarzan.
5. Oxonian.
6. The Spanish conquerors of South and Central America.
7. The Quakers.
8. Newcastle.
9. William Pitt, Earl of Chatham.
10. Centurion.
11. Maoris.
12. Black Peter.
13. Mary Arden.
14. Shrewsbury.
15. Marquis de Sade (sadism).

Names: Places, Things & Events
1. Equinox.
2. China clay.
3. Erin.
4. Reuters.

287

5. It was originally manufactured in Damascus.
6. West Point.
7. Ariel.
8. Eau de Cologne.
9. Pall Mall (after Pell Mell).
10. From the initial letters of the main centres where it was first produced (New York and London).
11. Mohair.
12. Pedometer.
13. Trooping the Colour.
14. *Daily Universal Register*.
15. Index (abolished 1962).
16. Sandhurst.
17. Reichstag.

Names: Shared Names
1. Flint.
2. Venus.
3. Nebuchadnezzar.
4. Newport.
5. Merlin.
6. Tyre.
7. Rochester.
8. Orange.
9. Phoenix.
10. Rugby.

Nicknames
1. Tommy Atkins.
2. One of the earliest steam locomotives.
3. West Ham United.
4. Joe Louis.
5. Fidel Castro.
6. Tibet.
7. Cats' Eyes.
8. Jumbo Jet.
9. Benito Mussolini.
10. Rookie.
11. Nessie (Loch Ness Monster).
12. The poet John Dryden.
13. Shirley Bassey.
14. George III.
15. Hotspur.
16. Edinburgh Old Town.

288

17. President and First Lady of the United States.
18. Lord Baden Powell.
19. Ten gallon hat.
20. Vera Lynn.
21. *The Times*.
22. Harold MacMillan.
23. Sir Christopher Hatton.
24. Napoleon Bonaparte.
25. A German long range gun.
26. Black and Tans.
27. Oliver Cromwell.
28. Beak.
29. Rudolf Hess.
30. Men's trousers.

Numbers
1. Six.
2. 13 red and white stripes, 50 stars.
3. 150.
4. 365 (Calendar Islands).
5. 600.
6. 22 trumps and 78 cards.
7. 2.
8. 368 days.
9. 5.
10. 191.
11. 319 billion (exact figure 318,979,564,000).
12. 127.
13. 79.
14. 27.
15. 81.
16. 54.
17. 'Seven for a secret never to be told.'
18. 101.
19. 450 days.
20. 127.
21. 14.

Nursery Rhymes
1. The Great Plague of 1665.
2. Honey and plenty of money wrapped up in a five pound note.
3. The Grand Old Duke of York.
4. Georgie Porgie.
5. Silver bells and cockle shells and pretty maids all in a row.

6. 'Old King Cole was a merry old soul.'
7. Among the cinders.
8. Wednesday.
9. Seven.
10. The Owl.
11. Vinegar and brown paper.
12. *This is the house that Jack built.*
13. A silver nutmeg and a golden pear.
14. Kitty Fisher.
15. Bells.
16. *Over the Hills and Far Away.*
17. Broth.
18. Frogs and snails and puppy dogs' tails.
19. Johnny Green.
20. A cold and frosty morning.
21. All the King's horses and all the King's men.
22. 'Are the children all in bed, For now it's 8 o'clock?'
23. Drury Lane.
24. Gentlemen.
25. Macaroni.
26. On a summer's day.
27. Cat, cow and dog.
28. A penny.
29. Old Mother Hubbard.
30. Johnny.
31. Full of woe.
32. Peter and Paul.
33. Butcher, baker, candlestick-maker.
34. Little Tommy Tucker.
35. Tommy Stout.
36. Nine days old.
37. 24.
38. In the corn.
39. A crooked cat.
40. Little Tommy Tittlemouse.

Ornithology
1. The Mute Swan.
2. The Missel Thrush.
3. Mauritius, or Reunion Island.
4. To the thrush family.
5. The Sea Eagle.
6. The Green Woodpecker.
7. The Kestrel.
8. The Great Auk.

9. Songthrush.
10. The Laughing Jackass.
11. Butcher bird.
12. The grouse family.
13. Snakes.
14. Goose.
15. A Cormorant.

Places
1. Dartmoor.
2. Disneyland.
3. Lincolnshire.
4. Arundel Castle.
5. Kent. (It is near Rochester.)
6. Fort Knox.
7. Morecambe.
8. Montmartre.
9. Oxfordshire.
10. Luxembourg.
11. Isle of Wight.
12. The Bridge of Sighs.
13. St Paul's Cathedral.
14. On the island of Skye – the Cuillin Hills.
15. Highgate.
16. Longleat.
17. Winchester.
18. Wells.
19. Salisbury.
20. On the River Thames at Woolwich (London).
21. Victoria Falls.
22. Blenheim Palace.
23. Palace of Westminster (the Houses of Parliament).
24. Mayfair.
25. Melbourne (Lord Melbourne).
26. The Tin Hill Inn, Yorkshire.
27. Hyde Park.
28. Ponte Vecchio.

Plants & Gardening
1. Busy Lizzie.
2. Transplant seedlings and small plants.
3. Venus's Flytrap.
4. Dahlia.

5. Clematis.
6. Pistil.
7. A pollarded tree.
8. It is the staple winter food of the reindeer.
9. Michaelmas Daisy.
10. Shamrock.
11. Osier.
12. Aphids.
13. Tine.
14. Hybrid.
15. Hardy.
16. Bluebell.
17. Mexico.
18. Peach.
19. Hydroponics.
20. Coconut Palm.
21. Japan.
22. Terrarium.
23. They are carnivorous.
24. Thrift.
25. The pineapple.
26. Bamboo.
27. Botany.
28. Yew tree.
29. Common poppy.
30. Tap root.
31. Kew Gardens.
32. Loganberry.
33. Brassica.
34. Pruning.
35. Catkins.
36. Dog Rose.
37. Succulent.
38. Primrose.
39. Chlorophyll.
40. A type of evergreen oak (Cork-oak).
41. Nectarine.
42. Daffodil.
43. Hawthorn.
44. Osmosis.
45. Spain.
46. The Egg-plant.
47. Conkers.
48. Node.
49. Variegated.
50. Saffron.

Politics: America
1. Lyndon B Johnson.
2. Abraham Lincoln.
3. Herbert Clark Hoover.
4. Theodore Roosevelt.
5. Michael Dukakis.
6. Gerald Rudolf Ford.
7. Milhous.
8. Monroe Doctrine.
9. Woodrow Wilson.
10. Ronald Reagan.
11. Dallas, Texas.
12. James Earl Carter.
13. Franklin Delano Roosevelt.
14. McCarthyism.
15. The elephant.
16. Spiro Agnew.
17. Gettysburg Address.
18. Freedom of speech and worship, and from fear and want.

Politics: Britain
1. Sir Robert Walpole.
2. The Liberals.
3. The Government Chief Whip.
4. Aneurin Bevan.
5. Clement Atlee.
6. June 1965.
7. Robert Peel.
8. 1973 (1st January).
9. Jo Grimond.
10. James.
11. Gerrymandering.
12. Neil Kinnock.
13. James Keir Hardie.
14. The Miners' Union.
15. Lord Scarman.
16. Harold Wilson.
17. Shirley Williams, David Owen, Roy Jenkins, Bill Rodgers.
18. William Wilberforce.
19. Red (those in Commons are green).
20. Sir Alec Douglas Home.
21. Prime Minister of Great Britain.
22. David Blunkett.
23. The Crown.
24. Ramsay MacDonald.

25. The Lord Chancellor.
26. David Lloyd George.

Politics: Rest Of The World
1. The Althing.
2. Seven.
3. Robert Mugabe.
4. Nikita Krushchev.
5. New Zealand.
6. Pinochet.
7. 1991.
8. Bismarck.
9. Spain.
10. Fianna Fail and Fine Gael.
11. Lech Walesa.
12. Joseph Goebbels.
13. Israel.
14. Machiavelli.
15. Sharpville.
16. Archbishop Makarios.
17. Zionism.
18. Jan Christian Smuts.
19. Menachem Begin.
20. Dáil Éireann.
21. India.
22. The Bay of Pigs.

Quotes
1. Abraham Lincoln.
2. '. . . this was their finest hour.'
3. Oscar Wilde.
4. Queen Victoria.
5. Charles II.
6. Cecil Rhodes.
7. J Paul Getty.
8. Mikhail Gorbachev.
9. Napoleon Bonaparte.
10. Nancy Astor.
11. Beethoven.
12. Noel Coward.
13. Andrew Carnegie.
14. Marie Antoinette.
15. Eldridge Cleaver.
16. Mark Twain.

17. Quentin Crisp.
18. Margaret Thatcher.
19. Mary Quant.
20. Winston Churchill.
21. James I.
22. Neil Armstrong.
23. Franklin D Roosevelt.
24. Greta Garbo.
25. Martin Luther King.
26. King George VI (following abdication of Edward VIII).
27. Herman Goering.
28. John F Kennedy.
29. Lenin.
30. Captain Scott.
31. Helena Rubenstein.
32. Benjamin Disraeli.
33. Neville Chamberlain.
34. Jawaharlal Nehru (India's first prime minister).

Ranks & Titles
1. Lady.
2. Dauphin.
3. Aga Khan.
4. Samurai.
5. Army: General. RAF: Air Chief Marshal.
6. Lady.
7. Superintendent.
8. Earl.
9. The Emperor of Ethiopia.
10. Infanta.
11. Duke of Wellington.
12. Master of the Rolls.
13. Earl.
14. Major.

Religion: Christian
1. Christ's resurrection from the dead.
2. The Poor Clares.
3. The Angelus.
4. Young Men's Christian Association.
5. Palm Sunday.
6. Charles.
7. The Moderator.
8. Icon.

9. The Last Supper.
10. The Church Army.
11. Egypt or Ethiopia.
12. Jehovah's Witnesses.
13. The eating of fish on Fridays.
14. The Carmelites.
15. Methodist.
16. Henry VIII.
17. Brigham Young.
18. Jesus of Nazareth, King of the Jews.
19. Paschal.
20. The Plymouth Brethren.
21. Eucharist.
22. Mesopotamia.
23. Westminster Abbey.
24. The Gideons.
25. Days set apart for fasting and prayer.
26. C T Russell.
27. Jesuits.
28. Ash Wednesday.
29. The Seventh Day Adventists.
30. Christian Science.
31. Letters from Pope to bishops on matters of doctrine or discipline.
32. Carthusian.
33. The Creed.
34. Good Friday.
35. The Swiss Guard.
36. Corpus Christi.

Religion: Non-Christian
1. Buddhism.
2. Up to four.
3. The Hindu religion – they are gods.
4. The Jewish religion.
5. Red, green and gold.
6. Shinto.
7. Suttee.
8. The Sikhs.
9. Druids.
10. Veiling of women and keeping them screened from the sight of strangers.
11. The Dalai Lama.
12. Islam.
13. The Star (or shield) of David and the Menorah.

296

14. In Mecca.
15. Albania.
16. Islam.
17. Hindu.
18. Kosher.
19. Rastafarians.
20. Attock.
21. Long hair, comb, sword, steel bangle and short pants.
22. The Koran.
23. The Wailing Wall, Jerusalem.
24. Fakir.
25. Buddhists.
26. Rosh Hashanah.
27. Ramadan.
28. The Vedas.
29. Buddhism.
30. Talmud.

Royalty
1. George III.
2. Civil List.
3. William III and Mary II.
4. The Coronation of Queen Elizabeth II.
5. Typhoid fever.
6. St James's Palace.
7. Philip Arthur George.
8. King Edward VII.
9. The House of Saxe-Coburg-Gotha.
10. Glamis Castle.
11. Mrs Wallis Simpson.
12. Woburn Abbey.
13. Princess Anne.
14. Balmoral Castle Estate.
15. Louis XIV, The Sun King.
16. Defender of the Faith.
17. George VI.
18. Gordonstoun.
19. Richard III.
20. Auckland, New Zealand.
21. He married a Catholic.
22. House of Orange.
23. The Duke of Edinburgh.
24. *Victoria and Albert.*
25. 1969.
26. First cousin.

27. Marie Antoinette (wife of Louix XVI).
28. 1984.
29. Princess of Wales.
30. Lady Jane Grey.
31. The Duke of Windsor.
32. The Prince of Wales.
33. Catherine the Great.
34. George I.
35. Prince Charles.
36. Sandringham.

Saints
1. Brazil
2. St Andrew's.
3. St Apolline.
4. St Nicholas.
5. 31 December.
6. St Thérèse of Lisieux.
7. St George's
8. St Cuthbert's.
9. St Martin.
10. St Aidan.
11. St Thomas à Becket.
12. St Crispin.
13. St Peter's Church, Rome.
14. St Francis of Assisi.
15. St Bernadette.
16. St Vincent.
17. St Matthew.
18. St Francis Xavier.
19. St Stephen.
20. St Anthony.
21. St Denis.
22. St Vitus.
23. St Mungo.
24. St Cecilia.

Science: Common Names
1. DDT.
2. Dry ice.
3. Riboflavin.
4. DNA.
5. Laughing gas.
6. The philosopher's stone.

7. TCP.
8. Ultra High Frequency.
9. Sulphur.
10. TNT.
11. Epsom Salts.
12. Morphine.
13. Gelignite.
14. Verdigris.
15. Salt.
16. Carbon.
17. Heroin.
18. Sulphuric acid.
19. Liquefied petroleum gas.
20. Light Amplification by the Stimulated Emission of Radiation.

Science: Solids, Liquids & Gases
1. Hydrogen gas.
2. Formaldehyde or formalin.
3. Amalgam.
4. Citric acid.
5. Manometer.
6. 24.
7. Ductility.
8. Nitrogen.
9. Bauxite.
10. Copper and tin.
11. Sand – soda – limestone.
12. Methane.
13. Ormolu.
14. Mercury.
15. Metallurgy.
16. Chromium.
17. Magnesium.
18. Acetic acid.
19. Galvanisation.
20. Helium.
21. Copper.
22. Sulphuric acid.

Science: Studies & Theories
1. Acoustics.
2. Ballistics.
3. Electricity and electro-magnetism.
4. Archimedes' Principle.

5. Hydraulics.
6. The Theory of Relativity.
7. Pharmacology.
8. Hydrology.
9. Genetics.
10. Seismology.
11. The study of the efficiency of workers in their working environment.
12. Atomic Science.
13. The production of very low temperatures and the study of physical and technical consequences.
14. Albert Einstein.

Science: Symbols & Numbers
1. Silver.
2. Hg.
3. Platinum.
4. Hydrogen.
5. Sn.
6. Pb.
7. Tungsten.
8. Copper.
9. Na.
10. Lead.
11. Au.
12. Cl.
13. 94.
14. Potassium.

Science: Terms & Equipment
1. Photosynthesis.
2. Isobars.
3. Decibel.
4. Wind velocity.
5. A mordant.
6. Plasma.
7. Casein.
8. Absolute zero.
9. Plankton.
10. Plaster of Paris.
11. The Richter Scale.
12. Barometer.
13. Saint Elmo's fire.
14. Catalyst.

15. Ammeter.
16. Fahrenheit.
17. The Mach.
18. Radiation.
19. Hygrometer.
20. Isotherms.
21. Lactose.
22. Geiger Counter.
23. Storm.
24. Chronometer.

Ships & The Sea
1. *HMS Victory*.
2. Admiral of the Fleet, Admiral, Vice Admiral and Rear Admiral.
3. Doldrums.
4. *Graf Spee*.
5. Eight.
6. *Gypsy Moth IV*.
7. *Endeavour*.
8. She caught fire in Hong Kong harbour.
9. The Blue Peter.
10. *Great Britain*; Bristol.
11. A tea clipper.
12. *Wasa*.
13. Six.
14. *Mary Celeste* (sometimes called *Marie Celeste* after Conan Doyle changed the name).
15. Larbord.
16. *The Mayflower*.
17. *Ra II*; papyrus reed.
18. Blue Riband.
19. Henry VIII.
20. *Discovery*.
21. Trinity House.
22. A German submarine.
23. The Spanish Armada.
24. Red.
25. Captain William Bligh.
26. Sir William Hillary.
27. It is rung at Lloyds of London when a ship founders at sea.
28. A 53 mile race round the Isle of Wight.
29. 1577.
30. The Danish Navy.
31. Clydebank.

32. 'Crew has mutinied'.
33. *Savannah*.
34. Wet, dry and tidal.
35. A raft made of balsa wood.
36. *Nautilus* (an American submarine).
37. Among the first successful steamships.
38. Coracles.

Sport: Athletics & Gymnastics
1. Sebastian Coe.
2. Pentathlon – 5 events; Decathlon – 10 events.
3. Tug-of-war.
4. 16 feet.
5. Hop, step and jump.
6. Floor, vault, parallel bars, pommel (or side) horse, rings and high bar.
7. Bob Beamon.
8. Shot put, discus and hammer.
9. Roger Bannister.
10. Dismount.
11. Lasse Viren.
12. Liz McColgan.
13. Nadia Comaneci.
14. The Highland Games.
15. Jesse Owens.

Sport: Cricket
1. 22 yards (20.11m).
2. Sir Donald Bradman.
3. 1550.
4. The Nelson.
5. Next to the wicket keeper on his right behind the bat.
6. Warwickshire.
7. A stump.
8. Gary Sobers.
9. 11.
10. William Gilbert.
11. Yorker.
12. Marylebone Cricket Club.
13. The score by a batsman of zero runs in both his innings.
14. Surrey.
15. Wisden.
16. Fred Lillywhite.
17. Googly.

Sport: Football
1. 1923.
2. Swindon Town.
3. Manchester United.
4. Southampton.
5. Fairs Cup.
6. 1872.
7. Preston North End.
8. 1970.
9. Arsenal.
10. Derby County.
11. Bolton Wanderers and West Ham United.
12. Stanley Matthews.
13. 1904.
14. Bobby Moore.
15. Elland Road.
16. Glasgow Rangers.
17. Argentina and Uruguay.
18. Heart of Midlothian.
19. Jack Charlton.
20. Liverpool.

Sport: Golf
1. 18.
2. Arnold Palmer.
3. 14.
4. Muirfield.
5. A match between two pairs in which a pair play the same ball alternately.
6. Troon.
7. Tony Jacklin.
8. Tiger Country.
9. Bobby Jones.
10. Spoon.
11. Two over par for a hole.
12. Archery.
13. Wedge.
14. Laura Davies and Nick Faldo.
15. Two under par for a hole.
16. One under par for a hole.

Sport: Horses
1. Doncaster.
2. The race is only open to three-year-old horses.
3. Newmarket.

4. Sulky.
5. Newmarket.
6. Kempton Park.
7. Longchamp.
8. Hickstead, Sussex.
9. Pato.
10. Flat racing, hurdling, steeplechasing, harness racing.
11. Ascot.
12. Two Thousand Guinea Stakes.
13. Kentucky Derby, Preakness, Belmont Stakes.
14. A horse that has yet to win its first race.
15. Three.
16. Ascot.
17. Cesarewitch.
18. Lincoln Handicap.
19. Charlotte Brew.
20. Twenty.

Sport: Motor Sports
1. Brooklands.
2. 24 hours.
3. Belgium.
4. Bluebird.
5. Monza, Italy.
6. Danger, no overtaking.
7. Drag racing.
8. Monte Carlo Rally.
9. Jim Clark.
10. Brand's Hatch.
11. Italian.
12. Indianapolis 500.
13. Silverstone.
14. Daytona Beach.

Sport: Olympics
1. The five continents of the world.
2. Ben Johnson.
3. Melbourne, Australia.
4. 1924.
5. 12.
6. 1984.
7. The modern pentathlon.
8. Mary Decker and Zola Budd.
9. 122.

10. 1984.
11. 1908 and 1948.
12. Baron Pierre de Coubertin.
13. 1964.
14. Ski-jumping.
15. Barcelona, Spain.
16. 1924.
17. Charles Daniels.
18. Robin Cousins.

Sport: Rugby
1. All Blacks.
2. Thirteen.
3. Tricolours.
4. 1897.
5. Cardiff Arms Park.
6. Australia and England.
7. 3 metres (10 feet).
8. After the symbol on their official tie.
9. Argentina.
10. Wallabies.
11. The Springboks.

Sport: Tennis
1. Fred Perry.
2. Czechoslovakia.
3. Michael Chang.
4. All England Croquet Club.
5. Stefan Edberg.
6. Virginia Wade.
7. Steffi Graf.
8. Alleys.
9. Bjorn Borg.
10. Fed Cup.
11. Deuce.
12. Boris Becker and Michael Stich.

Sport: Various
1. Six arrows landing in the gold.
2. Batting, fielding and pitching.
3. 11.
4. 2.
5. Captain Matthew Webb.

6. A peak over 3,000 feet.
7. The Automatic Helmsman.
8. 6.
9. She was the first female cox in its history.
10. Sweden.
11. 147.
12. Alpenstock.
13. 7.
14. First played at Great Badminton, Gloucestershire.
15. 3.
16. Foil, épée and sabre.
17. 10 a side for men; 12 a side for women.
18. Hot-dogging.
19. Gold (centre), then red, blue, black and white.
20. 2.
21. 7.
22. 6 points.
23. 7.
24. Sweden.
25. 9.
26. The Squat, Bench Press and Deadlift.
27. The bullpen.
28. 4.
29. Feather-weight.
30. 8.

Sports: Events & Trophies
1. It was made out of rupees left in the bank by the disbanded Calcutta Rugby Club in 1878.
2. Jules Rimet Trophy (soccer's World Cup).
3. Rodeo.
4. Show-jumping.
5. Rugby League.
6. The University Boat Race.
7. Gaelic football.
8. Every four years.
9. Tennis.
10. Sky diving (parachuting).
11. Table tennis.
12. Horse racing (Australia).
13. Every two years.
14. Rowing.
15. Curling.
16. Ice hockey.
17. Major long-distance swims.

18. Rugby Union.
19. The Waterloo Cup.
20. Squash.
21. Golf.
22. After the yacht *America* which won it in 1851.
23. Seaplanes.
24. Darts.

Sports: General

1. At the members' entrance to Lords Cricket Ground.
2. Swimming.
3. 11 December – 11 August.
4. St Moritz.
5. Pelé.
6. Jackie Stewart.
7. 53 miles.
8. Empty hand.
9. On a billiard (snooker) table.
10. Stoolball.
11. Aviemore.
12. The caber.
13. Hurling (or hurley).
14. Canada.
15. A stoop.
16. Dr Jigoro Kano.
17. First man to sail non-stop and single-handed around the world.
18. Mexican. (Dionicio Ceron.)
19. Houston, Texas.
20. Spain (in the Basque region).
21. Revolving silhouettes.
22. Quoits.
23. International Tennis Federation.
24. 11.

Sports: Sporting Terms

1. Baseball.
2. Polo.
3. Trampolining.
4. Golf.
5. Curling.
6. Rifle shooting.
7. Boxing.
8. Ice Figure Skating.
9. International long-distance canoeing.

307

10. Volleyball.
11. Fencing.
12. Motor rallying.
13. Archery.
14. Basketball.
15. Ten-pin bowling.
16. Skiing.
17. Cricket.
18. Gymnastics.
19. Ice hockey.
20. Mountaineering.
21. Badminton.
22. Rowing or sculling.

Sports: Which Sport?
1. Skiing.
2. Showjumping and Horse Trials.
3. Baseball.
4. Rowing.
5. Pelota or Jai Alai.
6. Cycling.
7. Rifle shooting.
8. Horse racing.
9. Polo.
10. Ice hockey.
11. Canoeing.
12. Trampolining.
13. Archery.
14. Golf.
15. Irish hockey.

Theatre: Actors & Performers
1. Humphrey Bogart.
2. Harry Lauder.
3. Mime.
4. Bud Flanagan.
5. Sarah Bernhardt.
6. Tommy Steele.
7. Dame Sybil Thorndike.
8. Dame Ninette de Valois.
9. Harry Houdini (the great escapologist).
10. Robert Baddeley.
11. Barry Humphries.
12. Rudolf Nureyev.

13. Laurence Olivier.
14. Tommy Trinder.
15. Charles Blondin.
16. Eddie Calvert.
17. Mary Pickford.
18. Alicia Markova.
19. Coco the Clown.
20. Sir Henry Irving.
21. Mickey Rooney.
22. Billie Holiday.
23. Jack Benny.
24. Edith Piaf.
25. Mata Hari.
26. George (Burns) and Gracie (Allen).
27. Ivor Novello.
28. Anna Pavlova.

Theatre: General
1. *The Stage*.
2. Folies Bergères.
3. Oberammergau.
4. Farce.
5. Royal Academy of Dramatic Arts.
6. Tony (the Antoinette Perry Awards).
7. Barnum and Bailey's Circus.
8. Columbine.
9. *Phantom of the Opera*.
10. Walter Plinge (in Britain, or George Spelvin in America).
11. *Evita*.
12. Abbey Theatre.
13. 'Break a leg.'
14. Catwalk.
15. The Globe Theatre.
16. Joan Littlewood.
17. *Barnum*.
18. Vaudeville.
19. The Mermaid Theatre.
20. Above the stage, where scenery is stored out of sight of the audience.

Theatre: Plays and Playwrights
1. Arthur Miller.
2. Christopher Fry.
3. Harold Pinter.

4. *Private Lives*.
5. John Osborne's.
6. Tennessee Williams.
7. J M Barrie.
8. 37.
9. Agatha Christie.
10. Sean O'Casey.
11. Alan Ayckbourn.
12. Henrik Ibsen.
13. William Congreve.
14. Tom Stoppard.
15. *Waiting for Godot*.
16. George Bernard Shaw.
17. Anton Chekhov.
18. Arnold Wesker.
19. Noel Coward.
20. Mrs Malaprop.
21. Eugene O'Neill.
22. Jack Rosenthal.
23. Rudolf Besier.
24. D H Lawrence.
25. *Man and Superman*.
26. J B Priestly.
27. Tennessee Willams.
28. Terence Rattigan.

Transport
1. Silver Ghost.
2. Brown – Bakerloo; Green – District.
3. By balloon (first such crossing).
4. 1935.
5. Midas (also called black box).
6. It is shortened version of General Purpose (GP) Vehicle.
7. Dr Richard Beeching.
8. Veteran – all cars up to the end of 1918; Vintage – vehicles made between 1919–1930, inclusive.
9. Paris.
10. Railways.
11. Russia. (It was the ill-fated Tupolov Tu 144.)
12. Tachograph.
13. They were both originally aircraft companies.
14. Skytrain.
15. Rickshaw (or richsha).
16. 1970.
17. Victoria and Euston.

18. Austin Seven.
19. A helicopter.
20. Netherlands or Royal Dutch Airlines.
21. The reigning Sovereign.
22. It is worked by cable with a stationary engine.
23. Concorde.
24. Mercedes Benz 260D.
25. A Packard Tourer (dressed in imitation of a police car).
26. The Mallard.
27. Belfast.
28. Morris Garages.
29. Société Nationale des Chemins de Fer Français.
30. Euston.

Wars & Warfare: The First & Second World Wars
1. Battle of Jutland.
2. Rudolf Hess.
3. The Channel Islands.
4. Edith Cavell.
5. The Japanese attack on Pearl Harbor.
6. Kamikaze.
7. Republic of Ireland; Sweden; Spain; Portugal; Switzerland.
8. Access of the Baltic Sea via the port of Danzig.
9. The tank (1916).
10. Severing the mooring cables of sea mines.
11. He designed the Spitfire aircraft.
12. The Maquis.
13. *The Lusitania*.
14. *The Bismarck*.
15. The Maginot Line.
16. The invasion of Russia.
17. Fokker.
18. A glider.
19. *HMS Royal Oak*.
20. In a railway carriage in the forest of Compiegne.
21. Home Guard.
22. The Avro Lancaster bomber.
23. Lord Kitchener's.
24. They were all British heavy bombers.
25. At Yalta in the Crimea.
26. Admiral Sir John Jellicoe.
27. Vichy.
28. General Dwight D Eisenhower.

Wars & Warfare: Other Wars

1. General James Wolf.
2. The Crimean War.
3. 266.
4. The Boer War.
5. Admiral Lord Nelson.
6. China.
7. The Argyll and Sutherland Highlanders.
8. Saladin.
9. The Battle of Bosworth Field.
10. The Korean War.
11. The American War of Independence.
12. The American Civil War.
13. General Wade.
14. The Zulus of Natal, South Africa.
15. The Battle of Marston Moor.
16. King Edward I.
17. 1957–1975.
18. King Robert the Bruce.
19. First man to be awarded the Victoria Cross.
20. The Thirty Years' War.
21. The Iroquois.
22. The Battle of Culloden.
23. The bronze was used to make Victoria Crosses.
24. The Battle of the Boyne.
25. Sitting Bull and Crazy Horse.
26. Charles I.
27. American War of Independence.

Wars & Warfare: Various

1. The Kukri.
2. Marshal of the Royal Air Force.
3. 11th November (1918).
4. Edinburgh Castle.
5. A trident.
6. The Royal Company of Archers.
7. Antonine Wall.
8. The poppy grows in fields of Flanders where so much of the fighting of World War I took place.
9. 2.
10. Belgium.
11. Mickey Mouse.
12. The Athol Highlanders.
13. *Devonshire*.
14. A group of fighting men in the American War of Independence.

15. Argentina.
16. Buffer state.
17. Anti-Ballistic Missile.

Which Year?
1. 1954.
2. 1958.
3. 1975.
4. 1990.
5. 1848.
6. 1977.
7. 1987.
8. 1984.
9. 1840.
10. 1965.
11. 1991.
12. 1969.
13. 1994.
14. 1851.
15. 1982.
16. 1968.
17. 1961.
18. 1951.
19. 1993.
20. 1967.

Words & Phrases: Meanings
1. High fidelity.
2. Dress rehearsal.
3. It denotes a former Roman camp, fortification or garrison.
4. Chewed paper.
5. Dancing.
6. Advance Purchase Excursion Tickets.
7. A prehistoric burial mound of stones and earth.
8. Everybody is welcome.
9. Four.
10. Fire.
11. He walks in his sleep.
12. Testator (man); testatrix (woman).
13. Empathy.
14. Pain.
15. Good News.
16. Sacred carvings.

313

17. Infinite knowledge – all-knowing.
18. Highest point of the city.

Words & Phrases: Names
 1. Caffeine.
 2. Yokel.
 3. Stretcher.
 4. Leasehold.
 5. Heliport.
 6. Ombudsman.
 7. Gynocracy.
 8. Mummy.
 9. Stalactites.
10. Acrostic.
11. Reveille and Last Post.
12. Cartomancy.
13. Amulet.
14. A Dutch auction.
15. A numismatist.
16. Hara-kiri.
17. Flamenco.
18. Diapers.
19. Catacombs.
20. Chiromancy.
21. Splat.

Words & Phrases: Studies & Occupations
 1. Phonetics.
 2. Horses.
 3. Fish.
 4. Walking on a tight-rope.
 5. Fossils.
 6. Taxidermy.
 7. He is a dealer in horses.
 8. Caves.
 9. Beetles.
10. Screen printing.
11. Moths and butterflies.
12. Gardening or agriculture.
13. The art of dating past events by the analysis of tree rings.
14. The study of the formation and meaning of words
15. The principles and practice of making dictionaries.

Words & Phrases: Terms
1. Mafia.
2. Ecumenism.
3. Affidavit.
4. Onomatology.
5. Anagram.
6. Patina.
7. Cartel.
8. Elegy.
9. Gobbledegook.
10. Water divining.
11. Codicil.
12. Proxy.
13. Cartography.
14. Sabbatical leave.
15. In camera.
16. Subpoena.

Words & Phrases: Uses & Origins
1. Feeding sheep and cattle.
2. Stir porridge.
3. It was first made in the French city of Bayonne (17th century).
4. It is an acronym for 'port out, starboard home'.
5. Plant it.
6. Thugees (members of a religious organisation of Indian assassins).
7. The wages of Roman soldiers used to be paid in salt (salarium).
8. Drink it.
9. From Aprhodite, goddess of love.
10. To make her skirt stand out from the body.
11. From St Mary's of Bethlehem (a lunatic asylum).
12. Kings of Siam presented elephants to people they did not like – the expense of keeping it made it more trouble than it was worth.

Words & Phrases: Various
1. A medicine man or witch doctor.
2. It is the 'people's car', as ordered to be made by Hitler.
3. Joy-stick.
4. Bees.
5. Crucifixion.
6. Dormer.
7. Beads, made of shells, used as currency by some Indian tribes.
8. Coven.

9. Mice.
10. They are the old names for the fingers of the hand.
11. Scampo.
12. The Isle of Man.
13. Geneva, derived from the French 'genievre' (juniper).
14. Down a mine (methane gas).
15. Zenith.
16. It contains all the English vowels in their correct order.

Words & Phrases: What is it?

1. An open Eskimo boat propelled by paddles.
2. The rock and lighthouse on Unst, Shetland Islands.
3. A free pass to the theatre.
4. A fork used for pickles which has three prongs.
5. A mollusc.
6. A dance.
7. A bird.
8. A sunken ditch or fence surrounding a park or garden.
9. Enamelled pottery.
10. A toadstool.
11. A hot dry wind.
12. A firework.
13. A small barrel or measure of ale.
14. A type of spotted horse.
15. A beach hut.
16. A small round variety of plum.
17. A person's double or apparition (supposedly seen shortly before or after his death).
18. Savings or investment for future use.
19. A small ship.
20. An oriental pipe.
21. A small harpsichord.
22. A fish.
23. A sea bird.
24. An infectious tropical disease.
25. A musical instrument.
26. A breed of draught horse.
27. A volcano. (Stromboli.)
28. A large flightless bird, like an ostrich.
29. A small hunting dog.
30. A seven-stage watch tower, like a pyramid.
31. Inhabitants of southern Belgium who speak a French dialect.
32. A rifle.
33. A fish.
34. A West African baboon.

35. A breed of dog.
36. A type of cheese.
37. A jellyfish.
38. A book or gutter.
39. A large carnivorous beetle.
40. A Hindu nurse or lady's maid.
41. A Hawaian dance.
42. A fleshy or pulpy fruit enclosing a stone with a kernel (e.g. a plum).

Running A Quiz Evening

To ensure a successful competition you need to be thoroughly prepared and set up, whether you choose to have an individual-based contest or a number of teams challenging one another.

If you run a team-based competition, then the quiz organiser should establish precisely the number of teams taking part well before competition night. Each team should be asked to nominate a team captain and provide the organiser with this contact's address and telephone number. The captain will be responsible for making sure the team knows the dates, times, venues and rules of the competitions and will take the final team decisions on the night.

The ideal quiz team consists of three members, although it is always wise to have a reserve or two in case of illness or unavailability on competition night.

A referee should be appointed in advance of the competition to give time for this person to become fully acquainted with the rules. Referees should be completely independent of any of the teams participating on the night. (The post should not be filled by the question master or scorer either, since both of these posts are too involved with the proceedings of the evening.)

A diligent referee will study the questions to be used in some detail and may even carry out his own research into ambiguous answers. In this way he can be prepared for all eventualities.

It is advisable to have a separate scorer. For the question master to also try and keep track of the scores is onerous – especially if numerous teams are involved. There are many different systems of keeping scores during the match and the scorer can, with initiative, devise his or her own system so long as he/she is totally familiar with it and can advise the question master or the referee of the state of play at any stage of the proceedings. The scorer may also want to appoint a scoreboard operator to keep the scoreboard up-to-the-minute throughout the competition.

The role of question master is obviously of particular importance to the success of a quiz competition. His or her 'performance' will contribute greatly to the success of the event. As with the referee, this person should be prepared for any possible variation of interpretation of the questions. Disputable questions should be weeded out and discarded before the competition starts. It is also wise to practise pronouncing unusual or foreign words so that they do not become obstacles on competition night.

The question master must speak slowly, clearly and loudly enough for all to hear. It is a good idea to check after the first few remarks that everyone can follow the proceedings by asking those at the back of the room or hall if they can hear. On receiving a correct answer from a contestant which the audience may not have heard it is useful to repeat the answer given. There is nothing more annoying for the audience than to hear a question and remain doubtful of the answer.

The approach of the question master to contestants' answers is crucial – it must be fair but firm. Part of this is to consider the time allowed for a contestant to answer a given question. A simple 'I'll have to hurry you' is usually sufficient to get an answer (or pass) but the competition should not be allowed to drag too long. A time limit should be agreed with the referee and this included in the rules. In conjunction with the referee the question master must also decide on the awarding of full or half points for a partially correct answer.

Finally, just remember: a good quiz evening should be fun for everyone.